# SELF-AIDS
## In English Usage

By

### L. J. O'ROURKE, Ph. D.

Associate, Institute of Educational Research, Teachers College, Columbia University;
Director, Carnegie-sponsored study, *Rebuilding the English-Usage Curriculum*;
Author, *We Talk and Write* elementary English series; Formerly Faculty
Member, University of Wisconsin and Cornell University

## THE PSYCHOLOGICAL INSTITUTE
### Post Office Box 1117
### Lake Alfred, Florida

PE
1111
.07
1951

# Table of Contents

iii

Reference Section, *Continued*

# Foreword to the Teacher

The mastery of good English usage in speech and writing presents different problems for each individual. Variations in background, reading habits, and associations affect the attainment of language abilities to a considerably greater degree than they affect attainment in other subjects of study. Added to these variations are those of native mental ability that affect all learning. It is apparent, therefore, that efficient and successful teaching of correct English usage demands a method that is flexible and individualized, adaptable to the particular needs of each student. *Self-Aids in English Usage* provides such a method. One of the guiding principles in its planning and preparation has been that the student should be able to discover and to concentrate his study upon the points that he himself has not mastered.

Another guiding principle has been the recognition that points of English usage vary both in seriousness and in difficulty of mastery. It is now generally agreed that some deviations from standards of correctness are much more objectionable and a much greater handicap to those who commit them than are other deviations.

On the question of difficulty, extensive studies conducted by the author over a period of years have provided data showing relative difficulties not only of different usage principles but also of different applications of the same principles. For example, two somewhat similar applications of the rule that a singular subject requires a singular verb are of widely varying difficulty. Records obtained show that 81 per cent of eighth-grade pupils correctly use a singular verb after a subject including *one,* such as *one of the men,* while only 14 per cent use the correct form of the verb after a subject including *neither,* such as *neither of the employees.* It is noteworthy that many of the most difficult usages are also those that authorities in the field of language usage agree are least essential.

The practical application of these important principles has resulted in the development of *Self-Aids in English Usage,* which embodies method and content that have been successfully used for eighth- and ninth-grade language courses, for high-school and college-freshmen review, for business schools, adult classes, and for training classes of employees in industry and government.

At the start of the book the student is given brief definitions and examples of the parts of speech and a few other fundamental grammatical concepts that are necessary to the understanding and use of correct English, with practice in recognizing them in sentences. This short introductory section is followed by drill exercises directed to developing habits of correct usage. The drills are organized into three parts. In the first part the usages treated are those that are essential for a passable degree of correctness in speech and writing. In the second part, usages that are of lesser importance, but that should be correctly used by educated persons, are drilled. In the third part the least essential correct usages are covered. Each part includes reviews and practice tests on the points covered in the section. The amount of drill given on each point has been determined with the aid of data as to difficulty which were obtained through the author's studies. Typical sentences that are spoken and written in everyday life constitute the drill items; every effort has been made to insure that the drills shall be realistic and practical.

Following the drill exercise section of the book is the Reference Section. This consists of clear, brief statements of the rules of usage, each illustrated by examples that make clear its application. At the beginning of the Reference Section the parts of speech and essential sentence elements are defined and illustrated, so that the student who is not familiar with these terms may acquire sufficient knowledge of them to understand and apply the rules of their use.

A final and important section of *Self-Aids* is the Self-Correction and Guidance Section. Here the correct answers for all the drill items are given, and each answer is accompanied by the number of the rule in the Reference Section that covers the point involved.

The organization and content of this book provide for individualized study with maximum economy of time and effort. The student, following the directions given on pages ix to xii, completes a drill exercise on, for example, verbs in Part One. He then turns to the Self-Correction and Guidance Section and compares his answers with those given in the book. The Reference Section numbers beside the incorrect answers that he has given show him just which rules he needs to study. He turns to them and studies them. He need not spend time on rules that he already applies correctly. Then he goes on to the next drill exercise. His correction of this exercise shows him whether he has mastered the points he missed in the previous exercise or whether he needs further practice on them. Subsequent review exercises show him whether he is maintaining his verb mastery or needs to go back for further practice. Practice tests which, like the drill exercises, are corrected by the student himself, enable him at frequent intervals to check on his progress. These are followed by parallel Progress Tests, administered and corrected by the teacher, which give the teacher an objective measure of each pupil's attainment and an indication of what points need to be emphasized for study by the class as a whole.

Numerous advantages of the above described organization and method will be at once apparent, but the more important ones may be stated briefly as follows:

1. The student who starts with poor mastery and whose ability is limited is enabled to concentrate on the most essential points and on the ones with which he has most difficulty. He is not handicapped by having to spend his time on points that he may never be able to master and that are of secondary importance.

2. The more advanced and more able students are not held back by someone else's difficulties. They can progress at a rate determined by their own ability and application.

3. Correction by students of their own work relieves the teacher of much of the clerical work of correcting exercises. Nothing except the Survey, Progress, and Achievement Tests (see page viii) need be corrected by the teacher. For the daily drills, a periodic inspection of notebooks or work sheets is sufficient to insure that pupils are checking their answers correctly.

4. The most important phases of usage are taken up first, and mastery of them is assured before pupils go on to less essential phases.

5. Older pupils and adult classes may use the book with a minimum of teacher aid, thus conserving time urgently needed by most teachers.

6. The book may be successfully used by individuals studying alone. For example, the employed adult may use it at home. Or a high-school student whose class work in English is on literature or composition, but who is deficient in usage, may be given *Self-Aids* for individual study.

A Survey Test, an Achievement Test, and Progress Tests for use with the book are printed in the Teacher's Manual, which is available from The Psychological Institute. Each teacher of a class using *Self-Aids* may reproduce these tests, by mimeograph or other method, for administration to the class. The Survey Test should be given at the start of the course and the parallel Achievement Test at the conclusion of the course. Comparison of the results of the two tests can thus form the basis for giving final grades.

The teacher should read the directions to the user (pages ix to xii) with the class and make sure that all understand how to do the exercises and to use the Reference Section. He should also impress upon the students that they gain nothing, but rather suffer disadvantage to themselves, by using the Self-Correction and Guidance Section to find the correct answers before writing their own solutions. It should be pointed out that such evasion of study will readily be detected through the Progress Tests, which the teacher administers and scores.

Many students learn to write correctly usages in which they habitually commit errors in speech. To combat such oral errors it is suggested that the methods described on page xii be employed. It may also be desirable to have some of the drill exercises on points on which oral errors are made done orally in class, either before or after the correct answers have been written by each pupil. The review exercises are especially usable for this purpose.

It is believed that, through the use of this book, teachers will achieve a noteworthy improvement in student mastery of English usage, and at the same time conserve a very considerable amount of their own teaching time and energies.

# How to Use This Book

In the speaking and writing that you do every day you make some errors of word usage, sentence construction, punctuation, or capitalization. Perhaps you make fewer errors than other persons in your group, or perhaps you make more. But in any case there are incorrect language habits that you need to overcome if you are to meet the accepted standards of good oral and written English. Meeting these standards is important for your success both in the work you undertake and in social contacts. This book is intended to help you meet them by concentrating your study upon the points that are troublesome to you; you study the points on which you make mistakes, and not those that you already use correctly. You thus overcome your language and grammar difficulties with the least possible waste of time and energy. By using *Self-Aids* as directed below, you will soon find that you are making rapid progress towards the goal of good English in speaking and writing.

The first drill exercise is on page 4. On each succeeding page a new exercise is presented. Simple directions are given at the top of each page, or a reference is given to directions on a preceding page. Follow these directions carefully. The exercises are of several different types, which should be done as follows:

I. On page 4 there are eighteen sentences, each sentence presenting two choices in parentheses. The following is an example of the kind of sentences found on page 4:

> We finished the work before Mr. Harris (came—come) back.

Only one choice in each sentence is correct. Following the directions at the top of page 4, decide which you believe is correct and write it on your paper beside the number of the sentence. Do not study, before writing your answer, the rule of English usage that the sentence illustrates. Write your answers for all the items on page 4. Then turn to page 185, in the Self-Correction and Guidance Section. Under the heading *Page 4* you will find the correct answers for all the sentences on that page. Compare your answers with the ones in the book. Draw a single line through each one of your answers that is incorrect. Beside each wrong answer write the number or numbers printed beside the correct answer in the Self-Correction and Guidance Section. On a record sheet like that given on page 183, note the number of wrong answers you had and the rule numbers that cover those items.

You have now found out which of the verbs in the lesson on page 4 you did *not* use correctly. Without spending further time on the items that you answered correctly, you can now proceed at once to find out *why* you were wrong in some cases and what rule should guide you in using the correct form in your speech and writing.

Turn to the Reference Section, which begins on page 108. Each rule in the Reference Section is numbered, and the number that you wrote after your incorrect answer is the number of the rule that will enable you to correct that mistake and avoid it in future.

Find the rule covering each incorrect choice that you made. Study each rule and see how it applies to the sentence in which you made the mistake.

In later lessons you will have opportunities to apply these rules again and again, so that you can observe your gradual mastery of each principle of correct usage.

II. On page 7 a second type of lesson, in the form of a letter, is introduced. There are no choices presented in the sentences forming the letter, but most of them contain errors in the use of verbs.

First decide what is wrong in line 1. Then decide how the error should be corrected, and write the correction on your paper. For example, suppose the first sentence were:

Mrs. Howell set down and talked to us.

Your correction would be: 1. *sat*

If a line contains no error, write *C* beside the number of that line on your paper. When you have finished the drill, correct your work just as you corrected your answers for page 4, record the results, and study the rules for items missed.

III. On page 9 a third type of lesson is introduced. This type is called a Reference Section Drill. It gives you practice in finding and applying all the rules that cover the items you have encountered in preceding exercises. Lessons like those on pages 4 and 7 are aimed especially at helping you to form the *habit* of using correct English. The Reference Section drills are planned to help you to recognize the principle on which the correct habit is based.

In the Reference Section drills, do *not* write any answers until you have looked up the rules that apply. To look up the rules, proceed as follows. Suppose the first sentence were:

John was always wrong, no matter what he (done—did).

Perhaps you feel sure that you know which choice is correct. In the Reference Section drills, however, the object is not merely to give the correct answer to the sentence, but rather to recognize the rule of usage that applies to the sentence and then to apply it. How do you find the rule that covers the correct choice between *did* and *done* in the sample sentence above? At the head of the Reference Section drill sentences is a list of rule numbers. Turn to these rules in the Reference Section. Read them over one by one. Notice the examples following each rule. You will soon come to a rule which tells when to use *did* and when to use *done*. Check this rule against the sentence, and be sure you see *why* one choice is right and the other choice wrong. Then write the correct answer in your column headed *Correct Form*. Do this for each drill sentence. Sometimes a rule will tell, for example, how to choose between the singular and the plural form of a verb, but will not specifically mention the particular verb given in the drill sentence. The rule gives the general principle covering all such verb forms, however, and so it is the rule to follow. On some pages, not all the rules listed at the top of the page are drilled. On other pages, some rules are drilled twice.

When you have completed the drill, check your work with the Self-Correction and Guidance Section.

Exercises of this type give you practice in detecting and correcting errors that you make in your speech and writing.

IV. The exercise on page 10, called a Review Test, is like the one on page 7, in that there are no choices presented. Correct it in the same way as the one on page 7.

V. At intervals throughout the book, practice tests are given. The first is on page 13. Each of them is in form very much like the review test exercise on page 10. To do the practice tests follow the directions given for the exercises on pages 7 and 10. Record the results on your record sheet, correct your work, and study the rules covering items that you missed.

If you are studying *Self-Aids* in a class, your teacher will probably give a Progress Test after each practice test. The teacher corrects the Progress Tests, which are similar to the practice tests that you yourself have corrected. The Progress Tests enable the teacher to check on your progress in mastery of the principles covered in the practice tests. Note on your record sheet your scores on the Progress Tests.

In your work with *Self-Aids, never* refer to the printed answers in the Self-Correction and Guidance Section until you have written your own answers to an exercise. To look up the answers before writing them would destroy the value of the exercise. If you do so when studying alone, you will cheat yourself and waste your time. If you are studying in a class directed by a teacher, each Progress Test corrected by the teacher will show your failure to master the points involved, if you have simply been copying the answers to drill exercises and practice tests. The printed answers are valuable to you only after you have first tried to give the correct answers yourself. Then the printed answers will show you exactly what points you need to study, enabling you to concentrate your efforts economically and profitably on the phases of correct English that you have still to master.

Many people who make few errors in English usage in writing make frequent errors in their daily speech. To overcome oral errors, you will find it helpful to make notes of the errors that you make or hear your associates make. From time to time, lists of errors heard might be compiled by your class, and the whole class might devote time to special study and practice of the rules covering the errors that are frequent among the members of the group. Of course, in reporting errors no mention should be made of the name of the person who made the error.

Another helpful method of reducing oral errors in English is to have a friend co-operate with you in checking on your mistakes. Whenever the friend hears you make a mistake on some point that you have studied in *Self-Aids,* he will call your attention to it, and you will do the same for him. Both of you will thus become conscious of your most persistent errors and can the more readily overcome them.

# Parts of Speech and Other Grammatical Terms

The classifications into which words are grouped according to their functions in sentences are called *parts of speech*. The different parts of speech are defined in the Reference Section (rules 5—14).

Names, such as *subject, predicate,* and *object,* are given to the parts of a sentence to describe their relation to the rest of the sentence (rules 1, 17a, 67, 68, 69, 71).

In the exercises that follow, practice is given in identifying the various parts of speech and in analyzing sentences according to their grammatical structure.

The following sentences are to be used in doing Exercise 1. Directions for the exercise follow the sentences.

1. The excited men listened attentively while their leader spoke.
2. Harry's study of mathematics and electricity is helping him in his new job.
3. Everyone who takes this course learns thoroughly a few basic mechanical principles.
4. "Oh," exclaimed Ruth, "I forgot that she was alone!"
5. Bob tries hard, but he never makes a high score when he is playing with anyone except you or me.
6. A large reward was offered by Mrs. Allen for the return of the papers that she had carelessly lost.

*Exercise 1.* On a sheet of paper write eight headings, as follows: Nouns, Pronouns, Verbs, Adjectives, Adverbs, Prepositions, Conjunctions, Interjections. Then write each word in each of the first three sentences under the correct heading.

Example. John turned quickly to his sister when he heard the loud noise.

| *Nouns* | *Pron.* | *Verbs* | *Adj.* | *Adv.* | *Prep.* | *Conj.* | *Interj.* |
|---------|---------|---------|--------|--------|---------|---------|-----------|
| John | his | turned | the | quickly | to | when | |
| sister | he | heard | loud | | | | |
| noise | | | | | | | |

1

Then check your work with the Self-Correction and Guidance Section (page 184). If you made any mistakes, turn to the rules indicated and study them. Then go on to sentences 4 to 6 and list all the words in them according to parts of speech. Check your work with the Self-Correction and Guidance Section.

Sentences 7 to 15 are to be used in doing Exercises 2 to 10, which give practice in analyzing the grammatical structure of sentences. When you have finished these exercises, check your work with the answers given on pages 184 and 185.

7. My brother Charles will write Harold a letter in a few days.

8. Yesterday a girl from Indiana interviewed Mr. Sims about a job.

9. All the men who had passed the test went to the plant and began to work immediately.

10. Carlton and his brother told us that they couldn't come to the meeting.

11. Whoever made this model is an expert craftsman and has real scientific ability.

12. Martin showed Florence the phonograph and Mrs. Cole gave her some records to play.

13. We had expected the shipment on Wednesday, but now we can not promise you delivery before Monday.

14. The man who has offered to show us how to repair the radio is Ferris.

15. After a few months' training, Joan will be an expert stenographer; then she will be able to apply for the job she wants.

*Exercise 2.* Write the subject of each of sentences 7, 8, 9, 10, and 11. Then write the predicate of each sentence.

*Exercise 3.* Write the number of each of sentences 7, 8, 10, 11, and 13 in a column. Beside each number write the prepositional phrase or phrases that you find in that sentence. If the sentence does not contain any prepositional phrase, write "none."

*Exercise 4.* Write the number of each of sentences 9, 10, 11, 12, and 14 in a column. Beside each number write the subordinate clause that you find in that sentence. If the sentence does not contain a subordinate clause, write "none."

*Exercise 5.* Write the numbers of sentences 7, 8, 9, 11, 12, 13, 14, and 15. Beside each number write the kind of sentence it is grammatically, that is, simple, complex, or compound.

*Exercise 6.* List all the direct objects of verbs in sentences 8, 10, 11, 12, and 13. Remember that subordinate clauses, as well as single words, may be objects of verbs.

*Exercise 7.* List all the nouns and pronouns in sentences 7, 10, 12, 13, and 14 that are the indirect objects of verbs.

*Exercise 8.* Some of sentences 7 to 15 contain predicate nominatives. Write the number of each such sentence, and beside it write the predicate nominative.

*Exercise 9.* List all the verbs in sentences 7, 9, 11, 13, 14, and 15. Beside each verb write its tense, for example, "present," "past perfect," or "future."

*Exercise 10.* Write the numbers of sentences 9, 10, 12, 14, and 15. Beside each number write the infinitive or infinitives in that sentence. If the sentence does not contain any infinitive, write "none."

# PART ONE

## Verbs

Write numbers on a strip of paper to correspond to the numbers before the sentences on this page. Write your answers on your strip of paper; do not write on this page.

In each of the following sentences there are two or more words or groups of words in parentheses. Only one of these forms is correct. After number 1 on your strip of paper write the correct form for the first sentence. After number 2 write the correct form for the second sentence. Write answers for the other sentences.

Example: They have (gone—went) home._____*gone*

1. Has Miss Brown (went—gone) to the post office?
2. Five orders for these pens have (come—came) in this morning.
3. That man has (ran—run) for Congress three times.
4. The painters have (ate—eaten) their lunch and have gone back to work.
5. The audience applauded wildly whenever Lily Pons (sang—sung).
6. Three of the glasses were (broken—broke) when we received them.
7. I understand that the firm has (drawn—drew) up a new contract.
8. Miss Baxter (seen—saw) that the mistake was not my fault.
9. Parks was proud of the vegetables he had (grew—grown) in his garden.
10. The committee has (chose—chosen) Jim Bradford for chairman.
11. Barnes (did—done) a good job in checking these figures.
12. The contractor won't begin work while the ground is (froze—frozen).
13. Prices of those items had already (begun—began) to increase.
14. If he had (rode—ridden) to work, he would have been on time.
15. He (did—done) everything possible to satisfy the customer.
16. If we had (knew—known) your address, we could have wired you.
17. The supervisor has (spoke—spoken) about you to the vice president.
18. Mr. Nelson has (took—taken) two copies of the report.

4

# Verbs

For directions and example, see page 4.

1. Mrs. Smith has never (worn—wore) the shoes.
2. The expressman (brung—brought) this package for you.
3. Mr. Carter asked Bob to (set—sit) the boxes on that counter.
4. Last week Tom (says—said) to me, "Where did you get that suit?"
5. Everyone (drank—drunk) some of the cold water from the spring.
6. Frank Todd walked over to the chair where Mrs. Dennis (sat—set).
7. When all the coupons have been (tore—torn) off, return the booklet.
8. The night workers have always (ate—eaten) in the cafeteria.
9. Before I could speak, they (start—started) to congratulate me.
10. You may (sit—set) on that bench until the ambulance comes.
11. Two boys have (came—come) early to help with the work.
12. Joe has (brang—brought) the wire we needed.
13. Wait for me while I (set—sit) these records in the safe.
14. The men have (gave—given) us all the information they have.
15. That bus (use—used) to be half empty when it passed here.
16. The investigator (saw—seen) that Mary was pale and nervous.
17. The manager walked in and (set—sat) down at his desk.
18. Yesterday they (brang—brought) Mrs. Gordon home from the hospital.
19. Miss Clark has (broke—broken) her own record for speed.
20. Jones (sat—set) the water cooler outside the interview rail.
21. The witnesses have (sworn—swore) that Jackson was not in the room.
22. Don't (set—sit) in this draft or you will catch cold.
23. Has Carl (brung—brought) those bolts up from the stockroom?
24. When he paid the bill, he (asks—asked) for a receipt.
25. Bernard is one of the most patient men I have ever (knew—known).
26. The detective (sits—sets) where he can watch the door.
27. I had (tore—torn) off the wrapper before I noticed the address.

# Verbs

For directions and example, see page 4.

1. Fred Hale wants you to (let—leave) him use your fountain pen.
2. (Lie—Lay) on this couch until you feel better.
3. John's accident should (teach—learn) him a lesson.
4. Insurance rates (rise—raise) when accidents increase.
5. Miss Harris (let—left) me arrange the new display.
6. After the oil had been added, the engine again (ran—run) smoothly.
7. The injured man (laid—lay) where he had fallen.
8. Several women (brung—brought) hot coffee for the firemen.
9. The janitor should have (rose—raised) all those windows.
10. I must have (ate—eaten) spoiled food in that restaurant.
11. How long does it take to (teach—learn) girls to operate this machine?
12. We used the tires until they were completely (wore—worn) out.
13. (Let—Leave) the boys help you with those packages.
14. By morning the temperature was (raising—rising) rapidly.
15. Did you want those notes that I (threw—throwed—thrown) away?
16. I hope you will (leave—let) me have a chance to do the work.
17. Why are these scraps (lying—laying) on the floor?
18. The training program is going to (teach—learn) us more about our jobs.
19. This is the first time the boys have (wore—worn) their uniforms.
20. At three o'clock Martin (says—said) he would have to go home.
21. All the cards (lay—laid) in neat piles ready for sorting.
22. Everyone should (teach—learn) to speak distinctly and pleasantly.
23. Mr. Grayson was (setting—sitting) in the lobby when I saw him.
24. Did John have breakfast before he (starts—started) to work?
25. Perhaps Marion will (let—leave) me use her pen, since mine is empty.
26. During that year my salary (rose—raised) twenty per cent.
27. His mother had (gave—given) him the watch for his birthday.

## Verbs

If any one of the numbered lines below does not contain a mistake, write C on your strip of paper after the number of that line.

If there is a mistake in the first line, write the correct form on your strip of paper. Then write the correct forms for the other lines. If there are two errors in any line, correct both. DO NOT CHANGE ANY LINE THAT IS CORRECT.

On this page consider only verbs.

Dear Mother and Dad,

1. I'm just about wore out after a day in the stock room. During the
2. last two weeks there have hardly been a moment's let-up from the time
3. I begin in the morning until the last sale is rang up at night.
4. My friend Walter, who started working here with me three months
5. ago, has had some good luck. The store owners have finally taken him
6. out of the stock room. There is at least two reasons why he is pleased.
7. One is that they raised his salary, and the other is that they put him
8. to work on the sales floor. He and I was hoping that both of us would
9. be promoted at the same time.
10. Walter never seems to hesitate over the correct way to say a thing.
11. He don't feel the least bit uneasy about meeting people or talking to
12. them. It wasn't long before I seen that he has something that I don't
13. have. I am going to talk with him and try to find out what it is. I
14. should have spoke to him before, but embarrassment or something just
15. wouldn't leave me do it. I begun to get over that feeling when Walter
16. got his raise. He has already taught me that knowing how to think
17. clearly and speak correctly give a person self confidence.
18. Well, I have written enough about myself. How have you been? Did
19. you hear Frank Crosley when he sung in Springfield last week? I know
20. you always used to listen to his radio programs.
21. Write me soon, if the cold weather hasn't froze the ink in your pens.

My love to you both,

Ted

# Verbs

For directions and example, see page 4.

1. One of the new machines (is—are) to be used by Miss Roberts.

2. He says the announcements (ain't—aren't) ready to be posted yet.

3. At the meeting Mrs. Ryan (spoke—spoken) on nutrition problems.

4. I am sure Bob would (of—have) helped you if you had asked him.

5. (Can't—Cant) Margaret type faster than Ruth?

6. Mr. Philips, the architect, has (drew—drawn) the plans for us.

7. A person (ought—had ought) to answer the telephone promptly.

8. One of the new books (has—have) several pages missing.

9. Will Miss Hanley (let—leave) you go home early?

10. If Joe had been asked to stay, he would not have (went—gone) home.

11. (Ain't—Aren't) they the fixtures you want?

12. The men (sworn—swore) that they would hold out until help came.

13. There (wasn't—wasnt) a card with the flowers that came for you.

14. Norma (hadn't ought—ought not) to spend so much for amusements.

15. Barclay (rode—ridden) as fast as the tired horse would go.

16. One of the mechanics (was—were) trained in Denmark.

17. The last thing I (says—said) was, "Seal them, but don't stamp them."

18. Mrs. Thomas and her daughter (doesn't—don't) like this pattern.

19. Amy (ought—had ought) to make out her income tax report soon.

20. John and his brother (was—were) among the first to arrive.

21. The fishing (had ought—ought) to be just right today.

22. Has that material (lying—laying) on the shelf been sold?

23. One of his secretaries (keep—keeps) all the pay-roll records.

24. Have you ever (saw—seen) a person so clever with figures?

25. Bernice (couldnt—couldn't) find the invoices for the shipment.

26. The weeds (grown—growed—grew) so thick they killed the roses.

27. It (ain't—isn't) right to drive on the left side of the road.

## Reference Section Drill, Verbs

Write the headings *Rule* and *Correct Form* on your strip of paper.

For each sentence refer to your reference section, find the rule which explains the correct usage, and write the number of the rule under the heading *Rule*. Then write the correct form under the heading *Correct Form*.

For this page refer to rules 21—23a; 26—30a; 36—40a; 58—61.

1. Before Jim went out, I (ask—asked) him when he would come back.
2. The mail has never (laid—lain) unanswered over the weekend.
3. Do you think I (had ought—ought) to mend your gloves first?
4. You had better (let—leave) Lawrence do some of those tabulations.
5. Carl (knew—known—knowed) the danger but he was not frightened.
6. Bob had to leave before he had (drunk—drank) his coffee.
7. Most of the girls have been (taught—learned) to do two jobs.
8. We have plenty of time; the train (ain't—isn't) in sight yet.
9. We have always (wore—worn) comfortable shoes in the store.
10. George, I thought you (was—were) working at the foundry.
11. Ted Morley and George Smith (is—are) to report for work tomorrow.
12. Frances (rang—rung) the doorbell steadily for about two minutes.
13. Several members of our club (live—lives) on this street.
14. Try to find out who has (took—taken) the wrapping paper.
15. The bread that Louise made did not (rise—raise) properly.
16. Carl and Ben appreciate what Mr. Tracy (did—done) for them.
17. Do you know how many carbons of this letter there (was—were)?
18. Robert told the police that his watch had been (stole—stolen).
19. Why (don't—doesn't) the letterhead carry our new address?
20. Freeman should have (given—gave) you clearer directions.
21. They (wont—won't) send a receipt unless you request one.
22. The soprano has not yet (sang—sung) her final number.
23. Mr. Cole doesn't think Ben could have (wrote—written) that letter.

## Review Test, Verbs

Some of the sentences on this page are incorrect. If a word is incorrectly used, write the correct form. If a sentence is correct, write C. DO NOT CHANGE ANY SENTENCE THAT IS CORRECT. Do not rewrite any sentence; make the least possible change. Do not change the meaning of the sentence.

On this page consider only verbs.

1. I like the color that Susan chosen for her new curtains.
2. We haven't seen Darrell since he was transferred to Chicago.
3. Miss Stokes will learn the women the new method.
4. That page was tore when I got the book.
5. The truck drivers said they was ready to start.
6. Stanley has wrote me a long letter every week since he left.
7. There is more new boxes on the lower shelf.
8. When we had eaten, the boys say, "Let's go to the movies."
9. Anne Jordan has a dictionary, but she don't use it often.
10. Most of the men had already gone when we arrived.
11. The salesman's arguments have finally wore down my resistance.
12. The firemen had some difficulty in raising the ladder.
13. It don't take long to learn how to put on bandages.
14. Have you seen the new golf clubs that Mr. Stevens give Bill?
15. Three of our best speakers was selected to represent us.
16. Forks had ought to be placed to the left of the plate.
17. There is plenty of room to set the jars in this cabinet.
18. The document laid unread because it was too technical.
19. It was after midnight when the storm begun.
20. This desk and that cabinet seems to be in the wrong places.
21. A few of the clerks in our office has started a bowling team.
22. Is there enough copies of the new budget for the Board of Directors?
23. The artist has drew several sketches for you.
24. We can do our work as fast as you and Beverly do yours.

## Review Test, Verbs

For directions, see page 10.

1. The letter John mailed to me on Tuesday hasn't came yet.
2. The airplane was so heavily loaded that it could not rise.
3. The new citizens had swore allegiance to the United States.
4. Ask Johnson to lay the samples on that work table.
5. Have you ever took a test like this before?
6. We called Miss Hubbard when we was ready for more material.
7. Our swimming instructor learned us a new stroke today.
8. He will put them away after he has chose the ones he wants.
9. The work will be much easier now that Blake and Harris is back.
10. Bradley told us that there was some important parts missing.
11. Anne won't be a good pianist if she don't practice more.
12. There had ought to be a policeman at this busy corner.
13. A few of his rare books were saved from the fire.
14. Filling that order hadn't ought to take much time, Ray.
15. Fenton's small shop has grew into a large business.
16. Henry and Byron was the leaders of our team.
17. Will you leave me pay for lunch today?
18. Frank is wore out from his struggle with the fire.
19. Martha thinks you have been working too hard.
20. The patient eat everything that the nurse brought him.
21. Helen don't seem to take any interest in the theater.
22. The telephone rung for a long time, but no one answered it.
23. Alice set her microscope on the laboratory table.
24. I had told Jones all I knowed about the matter.
25. We should have made him comfortable where he lay.
26. The directors have gave us time to think over the matter.
27. One of his helpers think he can take charge now.

# Review Test, Verbs

For directions, see page 10.

1. Don't Donald go to work today?
2. I wish now that they had learned me the correct method at the start.
3. Barton's crops growed much better than Donn's.
4. Carol thinks your friends has arrived from New Mexico.
5. He sworn he would never try to climb that tree again.
6. In this compartment there are a flashlight and a first-aid kit.
7. The cadets sung songs they had learned at camp.
8. Two dimes and a penny was all the coins Max had with him.
9. People had ought to see a dentist at least twice a year.
10. Taylor hopes he will be chosen for the advanced training camp.
11. Mother has risen the window shades to let in the morning sun.
12. It will be too bad if Bob and his brother doesn't come.
13. Clara should of returned the defective heating pad.
14. The maid laid all the towels on the shelf before she left.
15. Has Dick and Charles finished their work yet?
16. Elsie don't play tennis with us very often.
17. I wish I had knew how to give first aid last summer.
18. After the march the soldiers laid down to rest.
19. Why don't you leave us do some of your work for you?
20. I thought you was going to ride with us, Jim.
21. My cousin had an accident when he come to visit us.
22. Morton laid flat on the ground under the car.
23. I am supposed to go with Mr. Knox, ain't I?
24. They had seen the new coach but had never spoke to him.
25. With Florence at the wedding were Carla and Tom Abel.
26. They never found out who had stole the secret plans.
27. I asked Tom not to leave his coat here.

## Practice Test, Verbs

Some of the sentences on this page are incorrect. If a verb is incorrectly used, write the correct form. If a sentence is correct, write C. DO NOT CHANGE ANY SENTENCE WHICH IS CORRECT. Do not rewrite the sentence; make the least possible change. Do not change the meaning of the sentence.

On this page consider only verbs.

1. I was just going to wire you when your telegram come.
2. Will you set down and visit awhile?
3. The kite raised a few feet, then flapped in the wind and dropped.
4. Father brung some apples and nuts up from the cellar on cold nights.
5. Mrs. Brown and Claire leaves in the morning for New York.
6. That is the only part in neighborhood activities Anna has ever took.
7. I will leave you borrow my movie projector for tomorrow night.
8. There is a pencil and an eraser in this box for you.
9. The pitcher of water in his room had froze that bitter morning.
10. Leonard thought that he had lain his hammer on the bench.
11. George should of rechecked this column of figures.
12. Paavo Nurmi run almost twelve miles in an hour.
13. Martin sent word that you was coming home some time this week.
14. I didn't think another collection had ought to be taken up so soon.
15. When Luella asked Jane to come, she says she couldn't.
16. A hole had been wore in the rug where Max used to pace restlessly.
17. The policeman throwed his weight against the locked door.
18. Please take your father the pipe that is laying on the table.
19. Ashley and Edna has a new radio in their car.
20. Tell the movers to sit this lamp on the floor carefully.
21. Marion has always went out of her way to do me a favor.
22. Several of the cups in the set was smashed in delivery.
23. Wasnt there a special discount for cash?
24. Sam wants to leave school, but his father don't approve of the idea.

## Pronouns and Possessives

In each of the following sentences there are two or more words or groups of words in parentheses. Only one of these forms is correct. After number 1 on your strip of paper write the correct form for the first sentence. Do this for the other sentences.

Example: John and (we—us) will go _ _ _ _ _ _ _ _ _ _ _ _ _ _ _ _ _ _ _ _ _ _*we*

1. James and (we—us) will work together in this room.
2. The hunters saw (he—him) and his dog.
3. Miss Bryson gave you and (I—me) the keys to our lockers.
4. (They—Them) are the men who were here yesterday.
5. (He—Him) and his sister went to school with us.
6. Frank took John and (I—me) to a good show last week.
7. (Him and you—You and he) ought to have many interests in common.
8. Carol and (me—I) want to go to the game tomorrow.
9. Uncle Walt sent Ted and (I—me) a card from Mexico City.
10. (Them—They) and their companions he completely captivated.
11. (Those—Them) are the reports you asked for.
12. I don't think Herbert recognized you and (I—me).
13. (He—Him) and (I—me) don't know how long we can stay here.
14. The collision injured neither (he—him) nor his passengers.
15. (He—Him) and (she—her) have both won prizes this month.
16. (I, you, and Mary—You, Mary, and I) have been assigned to new work.
17. Mr. Lake has chosen Henry and (we—us) for his sales force.
18. Mr. Stone directed (them—they) and their helpers.
19. Wilson told George and (I—me) what he had heard.
20. I must notify either his firm or (he—him).
21. The lawyer sent (her—she) and her husband a copy of the contract.
22. Mr. Ellis called (you and she—you and her) into his office.
23. It was on Tuesday that (she—her) and I went to the concert.
24. (Them—Those) are the new tables for the physics laboratory.

## Pronouns and Possessives

For directions and example, see page 14.

1. Everyone except (me—I) goes to lunch at twelve o'clock.
2. (We—Us) new employees are to report at Room 307.
3. There isn't room at this desk for Clyde and (her—she).
4. Miss Ray transferred (we—us) girls to another division.
5. Kimball and (me—I) have worked eight hours overtime this week.
6. Let's keep this a secret between you and (I—me).
7. Phil took the girls and (we—us) to the airport.
8. The package was addressed to (he—him) and (her—she).
9. Mrs. Maxwell invited (us—we) Kentuckians to her party.
10. (Them—They) are the things we brought from the store.
11. No one was at home but (he—him) and his father.
12. (We and the Whites—The Whites and we) are planning a picnic today.
13. Martha can ride with (he—him) and (I—me).
14. Captain Dale congratulated (he—him) and (me—I) on our escape.
15. (We—Us) players are going to practice every Saturday.
16. There is room for another person to sit between (she—her) and Tom.
17. Talbert and Reedy defeated (he—him) and his partner in the finals.
18. The personnel director called (we—us) supervisors to a conference.
19. (They—Them) are the keys for the front and back doors.
20. These tickets were donated to (they—them) and (we—us).
21. When are John and (her—she) coming back?
22. Lyle sent (us—we) old friends some pictures of his new house.
23. No one but (us—we) knows about this place.
24. They nominated both (him—he) and me.
25. The club re-elected (we—us) three to the same office this year.
26. (Us—We) girls have often bought hats from her.
27. These invoices have been checked by (he—him) and (she—her).

# Pronouns and Possessives

For directions and example, see page 14.

1. (George—George he) filled out the forms you wanted.
2. A speech of welcome was given for (we—us) new members.
3. The children were asleep, so we carried their toys and (they—them).
4. Mr. Russell (hisself—himself) showed me how to make the report.
5. (She—Her) and (me—I) often have lunch together.
6. There are plenty of sandwiches for (they—them) and (we—us).
7. A special notice was sent to (we—us) committee members.
8. Tom and Bill can't do all that work by (themselves—theirselves).
9. Has anyone asked Miss Grant and (him—he)?
10. These are my books; (them—those) belong to Fred.
11. There are chairs for everyone except the speaker and (I—me).
12. Did you give Mrs. Holt the message from Anne and (I—me)?
13. (Machinists they—Machinists) usually get good wages.
14. Albert ought to get (himself—hisself) a new suit this spring.
15. The company has opened a cafeteria for (us—we) workers.
16. (My sister and I—Me and my sister) will meet you at seven o'clock.
17. Farrington helped (us—we) boys with the clerical work.
18. We are expecting the auditors and (they—them) at one o'clock.
19. Last summer Mr. Coleman employed (her—she) and (me—I).
20. These men are preparing (themselves—theirselves) for better jobs.
21. There is some disagreement between (they—them) and their partners.
22. The group will be small without (her—she) and her sisters.
23. You had better ask Merwin (hisself—himself) about that matter.
24. The court summoned (us—we) passengers to testify about the accident.
25. Leonard is very patient when working with (us—we) beginners.
26. (Us—We) boys are going to put in our applications.
27. (Mrs. Gray she—Mrs. Gray) couldn't be at the meeting yesterday.

# Review Test, Pronouns, Possessives, and Verbs

For directions, see page 10.

1. We have reports from everybody except he and Grant.
2. I seen Dick when I was in Meadville last week.
3. Preston and me went to the ball game yesterday.
4. The committee members set on the stage and faced the audience.
5. Yesterday the company give all of us identification badges.
6. The athletic council entertained the new coach and we players.
7. Dorothy has wrote an answer to the advertisement.
8. Them are the letters you are supposed to mail.
9. Why don't you have lunch with us girls?
10. That motor has ran much better since it was overhauled.
11. Thomas won't leave anyone watch him work.
12. We have invited they and their friends to our dinner.
13. Bob has wore his tweed coat for five years and it is still good.
14. Everyone in the stands was cheering we players.
15. You shouldn't lie too long on the beach in the hot sun.
16. My brother he made this radio for me.
17. Frank and Edward read that magazine every month.
18. The injured men theirselves said it was their fault.
19. These packages are yours, and them are for Robert.
20. The water level in the reservoir has risen several inches.
21. Warren showed he and I the results of the experiment.
22. Stanley says that Mr. Eaton has promoted you and him.
23. Davis is sitting those canned goods on the wrong shelves.
24. Tom and Henry they didn't go with us last Sunday.
25. We strangers were very unhappy in the city at first.
26. Jim and Glen thought theirselves lucky to be chosen.
27. We can't go yet because the girls ain't ready.

# Pronouns and Possessives

For directions and example, see page 14.

1. The (captains—captain's) orders were obeyed promptly.
2. (Them—They) and (we—us) are on opposite sides in the argument.
3. Both (driver's—drivers') versions of the accident were reported.
4. The golf club is open only to (we—us) members and our friends.
5. I have called several places, but I can't find Gilbert and (her—she).
6. Jack cannot explain his two (friends—friends') absence.
7. Gary hasn't kept any of the money for (himself—hisself).
8. You are to follow Mrs. (Lewises—Lewis's) instructions.
9. (The children they—The children) have a holiday today.
10. Mary wanted to ask (Jame's—Jameses—James's) advice.
11. A heavy snowfall had marooned the Parkers and (we—us) at our cabin.
12. Carl has charge of the (players—player's—players') uniforms.
13. Are (them—they) the rosebushes you planted last fall?
14. We have all our regular (customer's—customers') names on file.
15. Everyone is accounted for but (she—her).
16. That is Miss Graves wearing the (nurses—nurse's) uniform.
17. The investigator asked (we—us) clerks a number of questions.
18. (Him—He) and (me—I) agreed to share the expenses of the trip.
19. Lawson has spoken to the manager about you and (me—I).
20. Have there been any messages for (us—we) night workers?
21. The (horse's—horses) leap failed to clear the hurdle.
22. The heat and the long climb had discouraged (us—we) hikers.
23. Both (carpenters'—carpenter's) workmanship was above average.
24. The man had no right to detain you and (they—them).
25. The engineer could not see the (brakemans—brakeman's) signal.
26. Mr. Thorp gave (he—him) and (her—she) checks for the amounts due.
27. There are some (welders—welders') jobs open at the new plant.

## Pronouns and Possessives

For directions and example, see page 14.

1. Grace has had experience in selling (womens'—women's) hats.
2. If that boy isn't careful he will hurt (hisself—himself).
3. Where can I get a coat like (yours—your's)?
4. The forest rangers aided (we—us) campers.
5. The supervisor and (me—I) have to check all the time sheets daily.
6. Doris has been handling some of Miss (Jone's—Jones's—Joneses) work.
7. Miss Ferris went with (us—we) girls to the lecture.
8. The (salesmens—salesmen's) commissions amount to fifty dollars.
9. The foreman says that (us—we) apprentices are learning fast.
10. Donald put the slide rule back in (it's—its) case.
11. All the relatives have arrived except (he—him) and his brother.
12. The two (stenographers'—stenographer's) notes did not agree.
13. The girls sent (he—him) and (I—me) invitations to their graduation.
14. Mr. Burton is to go over all the (mens'—men's) records tomorrow.
15. The president appointed Scott and (I—me) to the civics committee.
16. Where did you put Miss (Fergusons—Ferguson's) letter?
17. Mr. Dexter sent a memorandum to all of (we—us) employees.
18. In today's mail there were letters from Laura and (he—him).
19. (Who's—Whose) notebook is this on the table?
20. Roland brought (we—us) girls some candy from New York.
21. The three new (employees'—employees) pay checks aren't ready.
22. (He—Him) and (her—she) have decided to go to Chicago.
23. (Colonel Bush he—Colonel Bush) is going to retire.
24. Our record is good, but (their's—theirs) is better.
25. The laboratory assistant recorded the (mices'—mice's) reactions.
26. There has never been any disagreement between (he—him) and (I—me).
27. Yesterday Mr. Perry wanted Stuart and (I—me) for some special work.

# Reference Section Drill, Pronouns and Possessives

Write the headings *Rule* and *Correct Form* on your strip of paper.

For each sentence refer to your reference section, find the rule which explains the correct usage, and write the number of the rule under the heading *Rule*. Then write the correct form under the heading *Correct Form*.

For this page refer to rules 77—77a; 78—81a; 82—82b; 95—96; 100—100b; 102.

1. Jack took the blame which was really (theirs—their's).
2. At the show Clark and (me—I) sat in the first row of the balcony.
3. The new tennis balls are for you and (he—him).
4. When the storm broke, (Jane—Jane she) foolishly became frightened.
5. The (golfer's—golfers') scores were even on the eighth hole.
6. Did the boys (theirselves—themselves) build the clubhouse?
7. Delighted, (I and Rose—Rose and I) accepted the flowers sent us.
8. The explosion knocked the firemen and (he—him) off their feet.
9. Our host arranged (us—we) guests in line and gave us paper hats.
10. Fred wrote Joe and (he—him) an account of his trip to Santa Fe.
11. Ted asked me whether (them—they) were the only nails I could find.
12. Only (women's—womens') hats are on this floor of the store.
13. When the news came, there was no one at home but Paul and (I—me).
14. The guard said (us—we) workers were to get our checks at once.
15. The tie he was wearing was (Williams—William's).
16. The time passes slowly for (we—us) patients.
17. There should be no misunderstanding between you and (I—me).
18. Tell Harry and (I—me) about your experiences in Australia.
19. Will you work with Gertrude and (he—him) at this counter?
20. I am offering him two helpers, Betty and (I—me).
21. The typists, you and (she—her), will have to work overtime tonight.
22. The building is beautiful, but I don't like (its—it's) location.
23. Did you buy these fishing rods for us, Leonard and (I—me)?

# Review Test, Pronouns and Possessives

For directions, see page 10.

1. Their progress was so fast that it surprised even theirselves.
2. The woman asked where she could find children's shoes.
3. Us listeners were asked to give our opinions of the programs.
4. Mrs. Porter will tell you which one of the trunks is her's.
5. Carl introduced Bob and she to his mother.
6. Policemen's salaries in this city are very good.
7. Dick tried to get tickets to the concert for her and I.
8. The five applicant's scores were carefully considered.
9. There is no one in the building now but the watchman and me.
10. Every spring the stream overflows it's banks.
11. You and me could finish that job in two hours.
12. Mr. Harris has asked us to have lunch with him and his wife.
13. The company is glad to have suggestions from us salesmen.
14. Mr. Wallace hisself answered the telephone.
15. Bradley sent they and their children to the free clinic.
16. Mr. Roberts holds we four responsible for all the tools.
17. The movie projector was the senior class's gift that year.
18. All the girl's names were separated from those of the boys.
19. Mrs. Prescott she wants to order another table.
20. Will you put this package in Dr. Lennox's car?
21. Those are the wallpaper designs that you may choose from.
22. We are having a special sale of children's sweaters.
23. We have found the employment records for everyone except she.
24. No one has seen him or she for a week.
25. Helen has lost her gloves and wants to borrow a pair of yours.
26. The neighbors and us are going to buy a lawn roller and share it.
27. We have ten telephone operator's jobs open now.

# Review Test, Pronouns and Possessives

For directions, see page 10.

1. How will the new ruling affect the office force and us?
2. There was a desk for each of we office workers.
3. Then Ted he came to our rescue with a flashlight.
4. The cashier told Mr. Garner and we what had happened.
5. What do you think about that new draftsman's work?
6. Mr. Bolton will transfer Jones and him to our Albany office.
7. Grandmother divided the estate between him and she.
8. The Colburns and us have been neighbors for five years.
9. Calvin offered us boys the use of his car.
10. Betty has suggested that the children go with Frank and her.
11. My men can do the work by theirselves.
12. Miss Smith will notify you and them when Mr. Monroe returns.
13. Bernard is a member of the stonemason's union.
14. Between you and I, John's idea doesn't appeal to me very much.
15. We give discounts to they and their families on their purchases.
16. These girls will be given saleswomens' positions.
17. There is some mistake in Mrs. Blacks bank statement.
18. Copies of the specifications were sent to him and we.
19. Miss Sanderson would rather take over my work than your's.
20. The two mechanic's time cost us ten dollars.
21. The profits are divided among we stockholders.
22. We like to watch the wild geeses' flight every spring.
23. The guard admitted we girls after we had identified ourselves.
24. Joe should have asked the boys and us before making his plans.
25. Martin hisself told me about his promotion.
26. Mr. Bennett told she and I his reasons for leaving.
27. Harry thinks us men ought to organize a baseball team.

# Review Test, Pronouns and Possessives

For directions, see page 10.

1. This blouse will not lose its color when it is washed.
2. Me and Jim will be here at three o'clock.
3. A corrected statement will be mailed to her and her husband.
4. Jack shot hisself in the leg while cleaning his gun.
5. We cannot find a telephone listed in John Hollis's name.
6. All the men except he and Walter have signed the petition.
7. This letter should go to Mr. Greens department.
8. In January the stores often have sales of women's coats.
9. We cannot expect Jane and he before tomorrow night.
10. Mary and Eleanor have offered to exchange their books for our's.
11. The editor would like to get news items from we clubwomen.
12. The guide showed they and their friends the secret passageway.
13. We called two doctors offices, but both doctors were out.
14. Our failure to hear from home worried we travelers.
15. I called she and Bob as soon as I had word of the accident.
16. All the mens' names should be signed on the last page.
17. We two have been asked to speak at the next meeting.
18. Florence and he will not be able to go with us.
19. The boys helped theirselves to the food on the table.
20. Between you and me, I think there will be a change here soon.
21. Everyone congratulated she and I on our good fortune.
22. Miss Nelson has been selling womens' hats for years.
23. Alice lent him and I the money we needed.
24. No one but I was at home when the burglar broke in.
25. You may put your hat on this shelf with her's.
26. This check will pay the children's school fees.
27. Our house is almost exactly like their's.

## Practice Test, Pronouns and Possessives

Some of the sentences on this page are incorrect. If a pronoun or possessive is incorrectly used, write the correct form. If a sentence is correct, write C. DO NOT CHANGE ANY SENTENCE THAT IS CORRECT. Do not rewrite the sentence; make the least possible change. Do not change the meaning of the sentence.

On this page consider only pronouns and possessives.

1. Miss Vernon and him will interview all the applicants.
2. Peter is to divide what is left between you and I.
3. Them are the tools that Harry brought with him.
4. All the volunteers names should be listed in alphabetical order.
5. As soon as the job was finished, Mr. Page paid we painters.
6. Everyone in the room knew he and his wife.
7. The girls laughed at theirselves when they discovered their mistake.
8. The supervisor rated Charleses work excellent.
9. Raymond has offered you and I tickets for the new play.
10. The speaker he kept everyone interested in his talk.
11. We use their telephone whenever our's is out of order.
12. Some delay has been caused by the longshoremen's strike.
13. Us New Yorkers have had plenty of snow this year.
14. The librarian told Anne and I the rules for borrowing books.
15. Both him and Mr. Carter think that the offer is worth considering.
16. Mrs. Parker gave we beginners some good advice on gardening.
17. Alex sat beside Gregory and she at the water carnival.
18. Mr. Morley wants to get the two buyer's opinions on this article.
19. Any new suggestions should be submitted to we committee members.
20. The club has organized a womens' auxiliary.
21. Miss Foster thanked us clerks for our co-operation.
22. Dr. Wilkins treated she and her sister when they were ill last year.
23. Are them all the white shoes that you have in stock?
24. Every branch office had it's own manager.

## Adjectives and Adverbs

In each of the following sentences there are two or more words or groups of words in parentheses. Only one of these forms is correct. After number 1 on your strip of paper write the correct form for the first sentence. Do this for the other sentences.

Example: He spoke (angry—angrily) ----------------------*angrily*

1. Jack drives very (good—well).
2. His manner became (cordial—cordially) when I mentioned your name.
3. He ran (quick—quickly) to the window.
4. The air smelled (fresh and clean—freshly and cleanly).
5. My cold has (steady—steadily) become worse.
6. Peter handled that difficult case very (good—well).
7. She could reach the alarm button (easy—easily) with her foot.
8. Sue remained (quiet—quietly) while the doctor set the broken bone.
9. Both of the engines in the plane performed (good—well).
10. I like to visit Mary because she always talks (cheerful—cheerfully).
11. The pie looked (well—good) and tasted better.
12. John appeared (sudden—suddenly) in the crowd.
13. The cry sounded (close—closely) at hand.
14. Your dog minds (good—well).
15. The prices at Fox's are (considerable—considerably) lower than these.
16. She cleaned the furniture (good—well) with pure soap.
17. His coat was worn (bad—badly).
18. He said he felt (uneasy—uneasily) after his operation.
19. He fought as (brave—bravely) as any Marine.
20. Mr. Blue seems (gruff—gruffly), but he is really kindhearted.
21. You may not do it (good—well) the first time you try.
22. The subway guard pushed us (rougher—more roughly) than was necessary.
23. The tone of the piano sounded (excellent—excellently).
24. These figures don't seem (correct—correctly) to me.

# Adjectives and Adverbs

For directions and example, see page 25.

1. He received (a—an) honorable discharge from the Army.
2. Your work was (neater—more neater) than mine.
3. She takes criticism (lighter—more lightly) than he.
4. We have never used (that—those) kind of lights.
5. The model looked (steady—steadily) at the camera.
6. The voice over the telephone sounded (urgent—urgently).
7. It seemed (a—an) ungrateful thing to do.
8. Sam reads (better—more better) than he writes.
9. Miss Wilson sang that hymn (good—well), I thought.
10. I have two pairs of (these—this) kind of scissors.
11. Max looked (listless—listlessly) through the snapshots until he came to a picture of a girl he knew.
12. They brought along (a—an) ukulele.
13. Dan's intentions were (better—more better) than his actions.
14. She will become a good cook (quicker—more quickly) than Susan.
15. We bought (these—this) kind of tennis balls because they bounce well.
16. With my new eyeglasses, I can see (normal—normally) again.
17. (A—An) igloo is (an—a) Eskimo's hut.
18. Never mind Sandy; his bark is (worser—worse) than his bite.
19. I was (nearer—more nearly) ready than you.
20. The clerk advised us to take (these—this) kind of boxes.
21. When questioned, Howard looked (blank—blankly) at the policeman.
22. Don't touch that, or you may get (a—an) electric shock.
23. They smelled smoke (distinctly—distinct) when they opened the door.
24. Bill prefers (that—those) kind of records to all others.
25. Her dress was (longer—more longer) than her coat.
26. (A—An) ape can stand almost erect.

## Adjectives and Adverbs

For directions and example, see page 25.

1. The missing key could not be located (anywhere—nowhere).
2. The bracelet she wears is (a—an) heirloom.
3. The (too—two—to) men in uniform are marines.
4. (This—This here) notice says the post office opens at nine o'clock.
5. Haven't those clerks (anything—nothing) to do?
6. Pens of (these—this) kind will not leak.
7. (These—Them) window boxes brighten the porch.
8. The roses in Meg's garden were (more bigger—bigger) than mine.
9. It was (too—two—to) dark to see distinctly.
10. The candy tasted (strong—strongly) of peppermint.
11. (Them—Those) clothes ought to be soaked before being washed.
12. Paul (had—hadn't) never seen the Grand Canyon.
13. Neither man (would—wouldn't) claim credit for the idea.
14. We have (a—an) upholstered chair that needs cleaning.
15. Please give (these—these here) cards to your supervisor.
16. There are (too—two—to) banks in the village, (too—two—to).
17. Nobody (is—isn't) tried in an American court without a chance to defend himself.
18. Wipe (them—those) ink rollers with cleaning compound.
19. I doubt whether we shall need any more of (these—this) kinds of oil.
20. (To—Two—Too) miles farther on, we came to a crossroad.
21. (Those—Those there) tires aren't safe to drive on.
22. The load was (too—to—two) heavy for one horse.
23. None of the men (had—had not) seen the blueprint.
24. I can do that job (quicker—more quickly) than he.
25. Get some of (those—them) twigs for our fire.
26. Michael wanted to be a pilot, (two—too—to).

# Review Test, Verbs, Pronouns, Possessives, Adjectives, and Adverbs

If any one of the numbered lines below does not contain a mistake, write C on your strip of paper after the number of that line.

If there is a mistake in the first line, write the correct form on your strip of paper. Then write the correct forms for the other lines. If there are two errors in any line, correct both. DO NOT CHANGE ANY LINE THAT IS CORRECT.

On this page consider verbs, pronouns, possessives, adjectives, and adverbs.

Gentlemen:

1. I wish to apply for the position of correspondence clerk which the
2. *Daily Star* listed today in it's employment column. The type of work
3. and the salary seems to be exactly what I want. I am a graduate of
4. Lincoln Commercial High School, where I took bookkeeping, commer-
5. cial arithmetic, typing, shorthand, and other courses of those kind. I
6. have permission to use my teacher's names as references.
7. Our vocational guidance director gave some other members of the
8. class and I a clerical aptitude test. He told me that in speed and
9. in accuracy I could hardly of done better on the test. Also, I have
10. always done well in spelling. During the past year everyone in the
11. class but I was required to take a review course in spelling.
12. The position of correspondence clerk sounds attractively to me,
13. since correspondence work would leave me put to use most of the sub-
14. jects I studied in school. Naturally, I dont want my training to
15. lay unused. One of my ambitions are to become a secretary, and the
16. experience as a correspondence clerk had ought to be good training
17. for secretarial work.
18. I am eighteen years old, of average height and weight, and have no
19. physical defects. I can see normal, but wear glasses for close work.
20. Please let me know whether I may report for an interview. If it
21. is not to much to ask, will you notify me by phone? My number is
22. Ashley 4263.

Very truly yours,
Mary Brown

## Prepositions

In each of the following sentences there are two or more words or groups of words in parentheses. Only one of these forms is correct. After number 1 on your strip of paper write the correct form for the first sentence. Do this for the other sentences.

Example: Where shall you (sleep—sleep at) tonight?_____*sleep*

1. Where was he (going—going to) when the car stopped?
2. If you will be (to home—at home) tonight, we will come over.
3. He got a loan (off—from) the bank to pay the mortgage.
4. Where could that dog (be—be at)?
5. Bartley was (to home—at home) when the news came.
6. The Red Cross received a contribution (off—from) every worker.
7. Where (were you—were you at) when I called today?
8. They would have watched the fire, if they (had—had of) known it was burning.
9. We got the idea for our pageant (off—from) an old painting.
10. The Smiths stayed (at home—to home) nearly every evening.
11. I wonder where Jean has (gone—gone to)?
12. Living (to home—at home) is pleasanter than living in a hotel.
13. Mrs. Smith borrowed a cup of sugar (off—from) us today.
14. All would have volunteered, if they (had—had of) been able to operate the teletype machines.
15. Where would you (go—go to) if you left?
16. Take her packages (off—from) her, please, Ted.
17. Mabel would have written you if she (had—had of) known your address.
18. Where might the truck (be—be at), if not at the loading platform?
19. They bought their house (off—from) a real-estate broker.
20. Anne took our coats, and told us to make ourselves (to home—at home).
21. I wish I (had—had of) thought to bring my checkbook.

# Reference Section Drill, Adjectives, Adverbs, and Prepositions

Write the headings *Rule* and *Correct Form* on your strip of paper.

For each sentence refer to your reference section, find the rule which explains the correct usage, and write the number of the rule under the heading *Rule*. Then write the correct form under the heading *Correct Form*.

For this page refer to rules 110—111; 116—118; 124; 130—133; 136; 141; 144; 146—147.

1. Aunt Harriet looks (cheerful—cheerfully) today, doesn't she?

2. Like our own nation, Brazil is (a—an) union of states.

3. It is too bad we lost (them—those) notes of the lecture.

4. Where is the light (switch—switch at)?

5. He seemed more sociable than he (ordinary—ordinarily) was.

6. None of us was (to home—at home) when the fire broke out.

7. His words seemed to Tim (sharper—more sharper) than knives.

8. If I had (to—too—two) dollars more, I'd buy that atlas.

9. When Anna cleans house, she does it (good—well).

10. You would have liked him, if you (had—had of) known him well.

11. Father asked me to bring him (that—that there) ash tray.

12. The natives seemed (angry—angrily) when the explorers came.

13. The bell sounded (sudden—suddenly) like a warning.

14. I always buy my pencils (off—from) the man at the corner.

15. Isn't there (anybody—nobody) here who can take shorthand?

16. Martin is (easy—easily) pleased by a little thoughtfulness.

17. None of (those—that) kind of locks can be picked.

18. How (fragrant—fragrantly) the flowers smell after the rain!

19. He never seemed more (considerate—considerately) than on that day.

20. Can he speak Spanish as (good—well) as you?

21. The garden smells (strong—strongly) of honeysuckle.

22. Try to express yourself a little (clearer—more clearly).

# Review Test, Verbs, Pronouns, Possessives, Adjectives, Adverbs, and Prepositions

For directions, see page 10.

1. The surface of the board felt smoothly to the touch.
2. If you nail them boards up, the fence will be stronger.
3. I thought there was some colored pencils in that box.
4. There is a great deal in common between him and her.
5. The swimmer was to weak to reach shore unaided.
6. Watches of this kind are made in Switzerland.
7. That man use to work in my office.
8. There wasn't nothing he could do when the rear axle broke.
9. John and she will be here tomorrow night.
10. Thieves stole a large sum of money off a local citizen.
11. That there basket holds just a peck.
12. Will Mr. Smith be to home tomorrow?
13. That last shipment was packed carefully.
14. They asked where the packages should be sent to.
15. The architect has put the girls lockers near the door.
16. If Abe had of failed, he would simply have tried again.
17. Burton has promised to do whatever he can for we three.
18. Tom wants to borrow the book you was reading last week.
19. You will find those kind of pictures in cheap magazines.
20. He has been to home ill every day this week.
21. I can't see a speck of dust nowhere.
22. Hadley was told to take his bills to the cashiers desk.
23. He fastened too hooks to the wall.
24. Most of the tenants were out when the alarm bell rang.
25. That there tree is shading the house too much.
26. These arent the correct figures for this year's salaries.

# Review Test, Adjectives, Adverbs, and Prepositions

For directions, see page 10.

1. He never believes nothing bad about anyone.
2. If the penguins of long ago had of used their wings more, those we see today would be able to fly.
3. We were pleased to see that the tomatoes were growing good and that they would soon be ripe.
4. Tom is more older than his brother Eddie.
5. I weighed the package on this here scale.
6. It seems too bad to be tardy, to.
7. Margaret prefers that kind of shoes to any other.
8. A lone gull flew slowly over the ship as we set sail.
9. Kate is too easy distracted when she is studying.
10. Where does the stock clerk keep them small rivets?
11. The box smelled faintly of sandalwood and spices.
12. No book couldn't have pleased John more than *Treasure Island*.
13. It was a hard decision to make, but a honorable one.
14. The employees quick became accustomed to the new conditions.
15. It wasn't no responsibility of his, he declared.
16. Ellen's hands and knees were bruised bad when she fell.
17. Several prisoners escaped off the work farm.
18. That there pencil sharpener isn't very sharp any more.
19. The drum major looked smartly in his brilliant uniform.
20. No one couldn't have done more in the emergency than Ted.
21. I can always gain weight easier than I can lose it.
22. My tea always tasted too strongly when Marian made it.
23. At dinner, Mr. Glass complained his tea tasted too strong of lemon.
24. Sophie wasn't to home when the inspector for the gas company came.
25. Neither of the boys had never been in Canada before.

# Practice Test, Adjectives, Adverbs, and Prepositions

Some of the sentences on this page are incorrect. If an adjective, adverb, or preposition is incorrectly used, write the correct form. If a sentence is correct, write C. DO NOT CHANGE ANY SENTENCE THAT IS CORRECT. Do not rewrite the sentence; make the least possible change. Do not change the meaning of the sentence.

On this page consider only adjectives, adverbs, and prepositions.

1. Walking is more slower than riding.

2. There wasn't nobody in the room when it happened.

3. He finished the job in an incredibly short time.

4. We get our books off the branch library.

5. These flowers smell sweetly, but I like those better.

6. The dress was made good and was cleverly styled.

7. Paste those there labels on your packages.

8. If you had of oiled the clock, it would have run.

9. The First National Bank wants too messengers at once.

10. The room appeared darkly and forbiddingly.

11. I thought them coats would not be warm enough.

12. The cure is much worser than the disease, I think.

13. She beat the egg whites good until they were stiff.

14. It rained so hard last night that we stayed to home.

15. He looked happily when he heard the news.

16. No one had no practical suggestions to make.

17. Margaret thought that the soup tasted queer.

18. If Jim had of been late, he would have missed the train.

19. The gun was an unique specimen of rare craftsmanship.

20. By noon, where will Tim be at?

21. Aunt Mary usually speaks sterner than Mother.

22. We bought these kind of candles because they don't drip **much.**

23. Don't try to borrow any money off Uncle Tom.

24. It frequent seemed as though it might rain.

## Capitalization

Some of the sentences on this page contain errors in capitalization. If a word that should begin with a capital letter is written with a small letter, write the word correctly on your strip of paper. If a word that should begin with a small letter is written with a capital, write the word correctly. If a sentence is correct, write C. DO NOT CHANGE ANY SENTENCE THAT IS CORRECT.

Example: Did you see him on sunday?_____*Sunday*

1. We have some viennese waltz records in that cabinet.
2. This is our new neighbor. he is a doctor.
3. The head of the company is Mr. s. t. Norris.
4. He was a kentuckian, born and bred.
5. "I saw you toss the kites on high
   and blow the birds about the sky."—Stevenson
6. Wasn't henry grey born in the british isles?
7. My father has forgotten the spanish he once knew.
8. Everybody likes the bright colors in these indian blankets.
9. I sent you an order on June 10. did you receive it?
10. The american library association awards a prize annually for the best children's book.
11. The book was written in italian.
12. The oldest city in the united states is st. augustine.
13. When I asked what time it was, Mr. Carter pulled out his ingersoll watch.
14. The federalists favored federal power.
15. Frank complained to the society for the prevention of cruelty to animals about the treatment of the horse.
16. The employees of the company were members of the c. i. o.
17. Both swan and ivory soap are floating soaps.
18. Mr. Morgan is very fond of french cooking.
19. Ed received a book of poems by t. s. eliot for Christmas.
20. Guatama was the first leader of the buddhists.

# Capitalization

For directions and example, see page 34.

1. The train sped through the high hills of the west.
2. The receptionist said, "here is Mr. Fox."
3. Charlie was laughing quietly as he read *millions of cats*.
4. The federal security agency has an office in baltimore.
5. There will be an early easter this year.
6. In the royal box sat king George and queen Elizabeth.
7. "I don't think," he said, "That the sales slip is lost."
8. All vacations were shortened that Summer.
9. "Breathes there a man with soul so dead,
   who never to himself hath said,
   'this is my own, my native land!' "—Sir Walter Scott
10. At the church we saw bishop Harper.
11. The car turned West off the highway.
12. A whole nation was reading *gone with the wind* that Summer.
13. With the Doctor was mayor Peterson.
14. "Don't take those papers," Carl warned. "they are confidential."
15. Judith has a job in the south now.
16. The senate will adjourn next week.
17. Two Winters ago we saw a splendid ice carnival.
18. Jim's father was a Captain in the United States Navy.
19. Next the orchestra played *the pines of Rome*.
20. Sam answered, "we are studying a book on office management."
21. The reporters found admiral Halsey on board his ship.
22. The n. e. a. is an association of teachers.
23. New Year's day comes one week after christmas.
24. Marie said, "the customer was right that time."
25. Walk East two blocks and then turn right.

# Capitalization

For directions and example, see page 34.

1. She read a paper on sir francis drake, the English admiral.

2. In the Spring new orders start coming in.

3. When the typewriter ribbon needs changing, i have to change it.

4. The motto of the Rotary clubs, which exist in many countries, is "Service."

5. "I will go," he promised, "As soon as my work is done."

6. Fewer letters are received on tuesday than on any other day.

7. The largest lake in New York is lake Champlain.

8. The home economics teacher warned us, "when the pork is still pink, it is undercooked and may be dangerous to eat."

9. Our civil liberties are protected by the constitution of the United States.

10. Have you read the book, *the moon is down?*

11. The librarian of congress will be the guest of honor.

12. Brazilians speak portuguese.

13. God is the eternal and infinite spirit, creator, and sovereign of the universe.

14. The pentateuch consists of the first five books of the old testament.

15. There are four democrats among the Aldermen.

16. Much brazilian coffee is served at north american breakfast tables.

17. The union pacific railroad is a Western line.

18. The w. w. Wilson Company is now having its annual sale of household furniture.

19. We must get an eveready battery for the portable radio tomorrow.

20. It was uncle William whom George resembled most closely.

21. The new Chinese ambassador was received by the president yesterday.

22. The mimeograph is broken. we shall have to type the notices.

# Capitalization

For directions and example, see page 34.

1. This decision came from the secretary of the navy himself.

2. He replied firmly, "there must be a way to do it."

3. Where is that new chart? put it on the bulletin board.

4. On the table lay a copy of *twelve men in a box.*

5. The magna charta established the foundations of English civil liberty over seven hundred years ago.

6. The boys were most impressed by Rodin's statue, *the thinker.*

7. Each Fall the club took in new members.

8. The Atlantic charter was signed by President Roosevelt and Prime Minister Churchill.

9. The empire state building is the tallest in New York.

10. north americans and south americans have many joint interests.

11. In genesis we find the scriptural version of the creation of the world.

12. Lesley intends to ask his Uncle for the job.

13. The american middle classes have a high standard of living.

14. In the far north the Winter nights are long.

15. In the old maps of the ancient world the names are in latin.

16. The Mississippi river is one of the longest in the world.

17. "I thought so once," he murmured. "now I know better."

18. Miss Archer has met lieutenant commander Frost.

19. The "r.n." after her name means she is a registered nurse.

20. Thanksgiving Day is always on Thursday.

21. "Archly the maiden smiled, and, with eyes overrunning with laughter, said, in a tremulous voice, 'Why don't you speak for yourself, John?' "
                                                    —Henry W. Longfellow

22. Victor belongs to the american chemical society.

# Punctuation

Some of the sentences on this page are incorrectly punctuated. If a punctuation mark has been omitted or incorrectly used, indicate the correct punctuation as shown in the samples. If a sentence is correct, write C. DO NOT CHANGE ANY SENTENCE THAT IS CORRECT.

Examples: Where did you put my purse. _____*purse?*

Since she was in a hurry.  She waved at us
and went on. _____*hurry, sh*e

1. This is the coping saw.  Which we used in making the jigsaw puzzle.
2. Carefully hung on the tool rack were pliers hammers chisels and saws.
3. Are you going to attend the meeting on Thursday.
4. The address on the envelope read "Jacksonville, Fla," which looked like "Jacksonville, Ill," to the postman.
5. "What Give my horse to a tenderfoot?  Never" Slim declared.
6. Mr and Mrs Mills belong to all the local civic groups.
7. James was not ill enough to need a dr.
8. His tools were always kept clean, sharp, and easily accessible.
9. Oh What I'd give to have an addressing machine.
10. He inquired what training the new job would require?
11. Carl raked the lawn Greg trimmed the hedge and Dick weeded the walk, in order to have everything ready before Sarah's return.
12. How quickly that letter was answered.
13. Kent assembled the pages Charles folded them and Bob put them into envelopes.
14. He asked how he could prevent a rope from untwisting?
15. He clamped the dull hoe in a vise.  In order to sharpen it with a file.
16. Testimony of FBI. agents sent the counterfeiters to prison.
17. He wanted to know whether he should use a screwdriver as a chisel?
18. The organization was simple flexible and effective.
19. It was eleven o'clock.  When I last noticed the time.
20. What good training you have had for this position.

# Punctuation

For directions and examples, see page 38.

1. Paul said, I can bring the tent and the blankets.
2. Buenos Aires Argentina has a greater population than Philadelphia Pennsylvania.
3. No the soldering iron was not hot enough to melt the metal.
4. Mr. E L Glenn, Sr, is head of our company.
5. I came to ask you Mrs. White whether you would cut this stencil.
6. Jim replied, I cannot make these percentages come out right.
7. What a surprise we got when we heard you speak on the radio.
8. The boys asked "whether I knew how to snare a muskrat."
9. Yes the shop will open at nine.
10. How many volts should a dry cell register.
11. The ship left Lisbon Portugal on Friday June 4 1943.
12. It was just five o'clock when I stopped work, Ralph said.
13. Lincoln's burial place is in Springfield Illinois.
14. In Middletown, trolley cars are no longer to be seen busses have replaced them.
15. "What was your last job Milton?" I inquired.
16. Yes the new plastic is completely satisfactory.
17. The contractor told us "that the building code prohibits any but licensed electricians from wiring the house."
18. "Oh Has that regulation been changed?" she asked.
19. The cat dashed through the door down the garden and over the fence.
20. He snapped the light switch, nothing happened.
21. Open the book carefully the first time so that the binding will not be broken, the instructions read.
22. On Monday May 5 we visited Williamsburg Virginia.
23. No the applications received after that date cannot be accepted.

# Punctuation

For directions and examples, see page 38.

1. "Dinner is ready now" Mother announced.
2. The conductor said, "Have your tickets ready, please".
3. "Bill sent the message, Henry replied, as soon as I got home."
4. "I'll write," Constance said "Will you answer the letter?"
5. Mark Antony cried, "Oh, pardon me that I am meek and gentle with these butchers"!
6. "When you come, I told him, please bring your estimate for the job."
7. "Watch that live wire" the guard shouted.
8. You can bring the figures when you come, Paul suggested.
9. "Come in, Miss French," he said "I want you to take a letter."
10. The witness testified, "He asked me, 'Is this train on time' "?
11. "The highest spot in American territory is the peak of Mount McKinley" Jack read "and the lowest is Death Valley."
12. On Monday April 6 1953 this contract will expire.
13. Joe answered "that there were already enough men on hand."
14. "There are two cases," she said "which require special attention."
15. "I have sent for a new supply of vaccine, the nurse told us, which should soon be here."
16. "When will the report on employment be finished" Mr. Barr asked.
17. "I have already made the salad," Ann said "It is in the icebox."
18. The Army-Navy football game took place at Annapolis Maryland.
19. I think Carl you had better clear the ashes away first.
20. "How long will it take the concrete to harden" Mr. Lewis inquired.
21. "I will order the lumber, the salesman promised, as soon as the bids are in."
22. Who was it that said, "The poetry of earth is never dead?"
23. Put these sheets in a binder, otherwise they will become disarranged.

# Punctuation

For directions and examples, see page 38.

1. "Mrs. Ward called, said Jane, to tell us that she is going to move."

2. What is your telephone extension number Bradley?

3. "I'm sorry I bought that secondhand radio", Philip acknowledged.

4. Sally said "that mushrooms are not only delicious in flavor but high in protein content as well."

5. Long vines trailed across the windows the doors and the porch.

6. The address is 1600 Pennsylvania Ave, Washington, DC

7. The O.P.A was established to stabilize prices.

8. What a lot of orders that advertisement brought in

9. "The duckbill" the explorer explained "is a combination of bird, animal, and fish, which is found in Australia."

10. He decided to use an extension cord.  Since the lamp stood at a considerable distance from the outlet.

11. How fast that new stenographer takes dictation.

12. The shipwrecked men sighted their first plane on March 15 1943.

13. In New Orleans Louisiana is an interesting section called the Old French Quarter.

14. "Great" he answered. "I should like that very much."

15. Well how much would a new drill cost?

16. I want three clerks to work on that assignment, Miss Stone said.

17. Mark wanted to know how electricity works?

18. You will splinter that board if you drill all the way through, Grant warned me.

19. George is the capt. of his soft-ball team.

20. "Who had the hatchet last" Clem asked.

21. He wondered whether the water pipes in the closed house had frozen.

22. "Do you remember," I asked "whether we locked the safe"?

## Punctuation

For directions and examples, see page 38.

1. When he wanted to use his tools again, Earl found them rusty. Because he had left them in a damp place.

2. Tomorrow Lois will be a good day to start house cleaning.

3. "The highest automobile road in the United States is in Colorado" Bob announced.

4. Some of us wanted to know "whether Willis had changed his mind."

5. We went to the farm to the lake and to the mountains that summer.

6. Two and two don't make five, Grandfather used to tell us.

7. Regular customers are billed monthly, others are required to pay cash.

8. Mr. Smith bought a bell, a dry cell, and some wire. Because his wife wanted a call bell for the dining room.

9. Carl where did you put the hand drill?

10. We asked the driver "whether the next stop would be Columbus."

11. He tried to find out why the overhead cost was so high?

12. We stopped to talk to the capt. after the lecture.

13. The conference adjourned at noon on Wednesday September 1.

14. All the window shades in a room should be at the same level, Mary told the new maid.

15. Well how can this instruction be applied most effectively?

16. We hurriedly washed the dishes dried them and put them away.

17. "Good heavens" said Mother. "Did I forget the salt"?

18. This advertising copy is poor and should not be used. Even though it is better than our competitors'.

19. The question was whether to use a wooden mallet or a hammer?

20. Franklin D. Roosevelt was born on January 30, 1882.

21. The men tried to reach John by telephone by letter and by wire.

22. "Drop it, Angus, drop it" Richard commanded his Scottie sharply.

# Review Test, Capitalization and Punctuation

If any one of the following lines does not contain a mistake, write C on your strip of paper.

If there is a mistake in the first line, write the correct form on your strip of paper. Then write the correct forms for the other lines. If there are two or more errors in any line, correct all errors. DO NOT CHANGE ANY LINE THAT IS CORRECT.

On this page consider only capitalization and punctuation.

## COLONIAL ETIQUETTE

1.  At colonial tea parties it was considered rude not to urge a guest
2. to have more refreshment every time his plate or cup became empty,
3. and equally rude for the guest not to accept the profferred food
4. he could be saved from repletion only by the observance of a little
5. custom which saved both host and guest from confusion.

6.  A certain french prince, who was unacquainted with local manners,
7. was invited to the hospitable home of robert morris, famous financier
8. of the american revolution and signer of the declaration of indepen-
9. dence. Over and over, as the visitor's teacup was observed to be empty,
10. his host insisted upon his having more tea cream and sugar.

11.  Pray, sir let me pour you more tea", Mr. Morris would urge.
12.  "No Mr. Morris" his guest would reply although you are exceedingly
13. kind. But I vow I must not indulge myself to such an extent."

14.  "What sir Would you put a slight upon my hospitality"? his host
15. would then protest

16.  With true european courtesy, the visiting nobleman accepted the
17. tea and drank it, until, after his twelfth cup, another guest, one of
18. the famous minute men of concord massachusetts, took pity on him.
19. Leaning over, he whispered that he "must put his spoon across his
20. cup or mr. morris would have to go on urging him until the tea and
21. sugar gave out and the cow and the well went dry."

## Sentence Structure

Some of the groups of words on this page contain errors in sentence structure. Write the correct form on your strip of paper as indicated in the samples. If a sentence is correct, write C. DO NOT CHANGE ANY SENTENCE THAT IS CORRECT.

If it is impossible to make a sentence from the words following any number, state what is needed to make a complete sentence.

Examples: Your request will be granted at once for a
new calendar. -------------------------- *Your request*
*for a new*

He is charming I like him. -------------- *charming, and I*
(or *charming; I*)

I washed the sweater with strong soap, and it   *Because I—*
shrank and so then I gave it to my niece.-- *soap, it shrank.*
*Then—niece.*

1. The company sold a car to a doctor missing on two cylinders.
2. The wastebasket was crammed to overflowing he emptied it.
3. When the retirement system was put into effect.
4. Dinner was late that night, and we talked afterward, then Al had to telephone, and consequently we missed the first show.
5. The messenger dashed in and out again. Without waiting for a reply.
6. The operator looked up the number for me. While I held the line.
7. In spite of Lester's taking every precaution he could think of.
8. The squeaking hinge annoyed Mr. Cannon, he asked that it be oiled.
9. I gave the information to the telephone operator, but she was thinking of something else when your call came in and she did not recognize your name so you did not get the information.
10. Will stayed at home on Friday. Because he was ill.
11. The baby knocked the ink bottle over, and the dog became excited and ran through the ink, and then he tracked it all over the rug.
12. A green woman's umbrella was found in the taxicab.
13. We cannot change our bookkeeping system at present. Although we like your system very much.
14. John recognized the man who had robbed him from his picture in the paper.

## Sentence Structure

For directions and examples, see page 44.

1. The tire was thin, it obviously would not be safe for a long drive.
2. The room was ablaze and the house was doomed. Even before the alarm could be turned in.
3. She was nervous and she fingered her necklace and so the thread broke and the beads rolled over the floor.
4. The ribbon is worn, it will have to be changed.
5. We finally reached the factory, and the whistle was just blowing, and we found that twenty new men had reported for work.
6. Sam stepped on the brake when a dog ran across the road with all his force.
7. A child stepped off the curb the traffic officer held up his hand.
8. Have just received an appointment to a good position.
9. Mother had been cleaning and she used some oily rags and she put the rags into a wooden box in the broom closet, and probably that was how the fire started.
10. The paper listed a room for rent to a gentleman with three windows.
11. The phone rang and Bob thought it might be Betty and he wanted to answer it first and he ran to the phone but it was a wrong number.
12. The plans were ready materials had been bought workmen had been hired.
13. Tom just left here to get some house paint on his motorcycle.
14. The window was stuck with paint and we could not open it so we pushed hard and that was a mistake and the glass broke.
15. He took two days' leave last week. Without asking anyone's permission.
16. In spite of production snags and labor turnover.
17. The cat crept softly to the hole the mouse quickly stopped gnawing.
18. After the explosion, the ship, shuddering like a stricken animal.
19. The clerk found for me the pair of shoes. Which I had ordered.

# Review Test, Capitalization, Punctuation, and Sentence Structure

For general directions, see page 10.

On this page consider only capitalization, punctuation, and sentence structure.

1. The episcopalians have selected this site for a new church.
2. Kate told me that a special-delivery letter had come.
3. "What nonsense" she exclaimed.
4. The Constitution of the United States was adopted on September 17, 1787.
5. No the sickness was not serious.
6. Judy was at home on the monday after the first tuesday in november.
7. The checker handed every customer an itemized receipt. Whether he asked for it or not.
8. Felix was commissioned a lieut. in the Marines last month.
9. It was Cairo Illinois where he was stationed, not Cairo Egypt.
10. Anne declared, "It's a case of 'Handsome is as handsome does' ".
11. The lights dimmed the curtain rose slowly and some latecomers found their seats noisily.
12. In *a tale of two cities,* Sydney Carton is the hero.
13. My father belongs to the chicago athletic club.
14. Greg stood up, spilling nails tools and wood to the floor.
15. Her aunt lived in Boston and her name was Sarah Hudson and so Mary wrote to her and asked permission to stay with her overnight.
16. The Republican nominee that year was Wendell Willkie.
17. The directions say to wash this sweater with lux.
18. My friends I have some good news for you.
19. The manager flew north last Summer.
20. Edward asked me where we three planned to meet?
21. "The best books," Ray declared "are mirrors of life experiences."
22. Because smoke was coming from the engine and the metal was white-hot.

# Practice Test, Capitalization, Punctuation, and Sentence Structure

For directions and examples, see pages 34, 38, and 44.

1. Shirley wanted a blue dress, and she wanted a brown one, too, and she couldn't decide which to buy, and she couldn't afford both.
2. A blue and white flag was run up outside the argentinian Embassy.
3. Yes lunch is ready and waiting for you.
4. The textbook was entitled *Our Democracy and Its Problems.*
5. He was an old customer I always liked him very much.
6. elsie and i found a special-delivery letter in the mailbox.
7. We left the city on friday night and returned late on monday.
8. Tell George what will happen if the inventory is inaccurate?
9. Warren asked indignantly "who had been using his slide rule."
10. Was it Scott who wrote, "This is my own, my native land?"
11. Annette dressed as spring, in a flowing, flower-bedecked robe.
12. When Jack was in the west last summer, he saw a rodeo.
13. Men I am asking for volunteers for this dangerous task.
14. Henry decided to drive to Albany.   Although the night was stormy.
15. We wanted a house with ten rooms two baths a garage and a large lot.
16. "I may persuade him," Arnold said, "to double the size of his order."
17. Boston Massachusetts is surrounded by many suburbs.
18. Mrs. Fredericks had four sons who were Captains in the Army.
19. The soldier saluted smartly as a Brig. Gen. passed through the gate.
20. On Thursday December 31 1942 he drew up a list of new resolutions.
21. "Gary is fond of good music," Mrs. Adams said, but he can't play.
22. "Have you an opening for an expert stenographer," the applicant inquired.
23. *The nine Tailors,* by Dorothy Sayers, is an unusual mystery story.
24. At what counter shall I find woolen children's playsuits?

## Cumulative Review, Part One

If there is a mistake in the first line, write the correct form on your strip of paper. Then write the correct forms for the other lines. If any line does not contain a mistake, write C. If there are two or more errors in any line, correct all errors. DO NOT CHANGE ANY LINE THAT IS CORRECT.

On this page consider verbs, pronouns, possessives, adjectives, adverbs, prepositions, capitalization, punctuation, and sentence structure.

Gentlemen:

1.   I am writing to ask whether you will repair the radio I recently bought
2. at your store? The set seemed excellent to me when I began to use it.
3. Distant stations came in good, and the tone sounded very satisfactorily.
4. Within three week's time, however, something went wrong. The set
5. don't seem to do anything now but hum squeal and whistle. A friend
6. of mine knows a little about radio and he checked the tubes and
7. looked carefully for loose wires but he couldn't find the trouble, so he
8. advised me to lie the matter in your hands.
9.   The guarantee which all your sets carries "entitles me to free repair
10. service during the first six months after purchase." Unfortunately, I
11. cant take the set back too the store, since I don't have a car. There-
12. fore, whenever one of your trucks are free, will you please have the
13. driver stop here to pick up the set. My wife or me had ought to be to
14. home most of next week. One of us will be here to leave him in. The
15. radio will be setting in the front hall.
16.   You may wonder in who's name the purchase was made when you try
17. to look it up. I should perhaps inform you. That although I myself
18. selected the radio, it was paid for by the Willows club, which pre-
19. sented the set to my wife and I as a gift on our fiftieth wedding anni-
20. versary. The radio was bought on Friday December 16.

Very truly yours,
Elmer Doe

# PART TWO

## Verbs

Write numbers on a strip of paper to correspond to the numbers before the sentences on this page. Write your answers on your strip of paper; do not write on this page.

In each of the following sentences there are two or more words or groups of words in parentheses. Only one of these forms is correct. After number 1 on your strip of paper write the correct form for the first sentence. After number 2 write the correct form for the second sentence. Continue in the same way with the other sentences.

Example: (Can—May) I sit here? _____*May*

1. Under the new rules, no one (can—may) leave without permission.
2. For ten years now, Bob (has worked—is working) in the steel plant.
3. The President, together with five Cabinet members, (was—were) here.
4. Every policeman and fireman (is—are) on the alert.
5. He was not (affected—effected) by the bad news.
6. Every woman in the community (is—are) aiding the Red Cross drive.
7. Since he started on this job, Jim (was—has been) prompt.
8. Each of the splints (extend—extends) well past Tom's elbow.
9. Many people (can—may) not afford good houses.
10. The drivers, as well as the owner, (is—are) affected by the order.
11. The tree (was—has been) blown down in last year's storm.
12. Each bolt and nut (was—were) checked carefully for flaws.
13. You cannot be (accepted—excepted) from a ruling of the company.
14. He said we (could—might) give a demonstration if we liked.
15. Each surface (was—were) cleaned thoroughly before paint was applied.
16. Neither of the tools (was—were) accurate, so both were rejected.
17. His secretary says that I (may—can) interview him at once.
18. Everyone eligible to vote (is—are) morally obliged to do so.
19. Mr. Gordon, along with two others, (has—have) promised to be here.
20. The corn crop has been seriously (affected—effected) by the drought.

## Verbs

For directions and example, see page 49.

1. *The Arabian Nights* (contains—contain) the story of Aladdin.
2. Tap and distilled water (look—looks) different under a microscope.
3. My brother, together with his friends at the office, (is—are) planning a boat trip this week end.
4. *Self-Aids* (is—are) written for those who wish to help themselves.
5. All the officers of the club (served—have served) one year since the club started.
6. If I (were—was) you, I should try to get a noiseless typewriter.
7. She is one of those persons who (see—sees) some good in everyone.
8. On the first of last month the new quotas (were—have been) announced.
9. If you (would have—had) looked up from your book occasionally, your eyes would not be so tired.
10. Neither driver involved in the accident (was—were) free of blame.
11. He is one of the men who (understand—understands) the problem.
12. The police would not have arrested Chuck if he (hadn't—hadn't of) been in bad company.
13. Mary's typing speed and her sister's (is—are) identical.
14. *The New York Times* (have—has) a Sunday book-review section.
15. If it (should—would) rain, the picnic would be postponed.
16. If he (was—were) in your place, he would act as his own lawyer.
17. A difficult and an easy problem (was—were) assigned in the quiz.
18. Everyone in the hospital (admire—admires) his operating technique.
19. If you (would—should) watch the ball, your game would improve.
20. The streamline principle is one of the factors which (has—have) increased the speed of modern cars.
21. You could do it, if you (should—would) try hard enough.
22. If you (should—would) be in an accident, notify the police.

# Verbs

For directions and example, see page 49.

1. The company (accepted—excepted) the employees' terms.
2. I have made two copies so that I (shall—should) have one for our file.
3. If this item (should—would) be unsatisfactory, we will refund your money.
4. If you (would—should) concentrate, you would waste less time.
5. He opened the book carefully, so that the binding (might—may) not be broken.
6. If the river (should—would) rise, the bridge would be washed away.
7. (Shall—Will) I order a new supply of carbon paper today?
8. If he (would—should) follow your suggestions, he could do much better work than he is doing.
9. Oil is used to lubricate machinery so that friction (will—would) be reduced.
10. (Shall—Will) we ask the Browns over to see the movies we made?
11. He (cast—casted) the fly onto the water just as the trout leaped.
12. Hill is one of the men who (was—were) chosen to represent the group.
13. The Gallup Poll (forecast—forecasted) a large Republican majority.
14. Where (shall—will) we put the new water cooler?
15. He wrote the return address on the envelope, so that it (can—could) be returned if undelivered.
16. (Will—Shall) we plan the dance for St. Valentine's Day?
17. Joan (burst—bursted) into tears when she heard the news.
18. The Navy (affected—effected) the safe removal of all civilians.
19. Hemmed in by the sheriff's men, the villain (cast—casted) about for a means of escape.
20. The cake would have been of finer texture, if you (had—would have) used less baking powder.

# Reference Section Drill, Verbs

Write the headings *Rule* and *Correct Form* on your strip of paper.

For each sentence refer to your reference section, find the rule that explains the correct usage, and write the number of the rule under the heading *Rule*. Then write the correct form under the heading *Correct Form*.

For this page refer to rules 24—25; 31—33; 40b; 42—42a; 45; 50—51; 54—57; 62b; 64.

1. If it (were—was) raining now, I should take an umbrella.

2. The bag (burst—bursted) and the oranges fell all over the floor.

3. In most states children under sixteen (can—may) not work in factories.

4. Last autumn I (visited—have visited) the West Coast.

5. Each of the men (has—have) exceeded this week's quota.

6. "Keep cool" is the first of the rules that (is—are) to be remembered in an accident.

7. A radio mechanic, along with all first-class workmen in other trades, (observe—observes) rules of safety.

8. If you (would—should) only listen to my side of the story, you would understand what happened.

9. For the last two years, snow (has remained—remained) on the peak.

10. Dickens's *Hard Times* (are—is) an attack on Victorian indifference to social wrongs.

11. The wound would have stopped bleeding if Jack (had—would have) used a tight bandage.

12. The prettiest, the most popular, and the most capable girl in each class (have—has) been selected by vote.

13. We could go by train if the planes (should—would) be grounded.

14. At what time (shall—will) I meet you for lunch today?

15. Either clerk (is—are) capable of taking charge.

16. Let me sign the pass now, so that you (might—may) leave at once.

17. Only very low incomes are (accepted—excepted) from additional taxation by the proposed bill.

18. The decision (affected—effected) a reversal of the club's policy.

## Review Test, Verbs

Some of the sentences on this page are incorrect. If a word is incorrectly used, write the correct form. If a sentence is correct, write C. DO NOT CHANGE ANY SENTENCE THAT IS CORRECT. Do not rewrite any sentence; make the least possible change. Do not change the meaning of the sentence.

On this page consider only verbs.

1. Each year since the business was founded, it showed a profit.
2. Will we have a chance to swim before dinner?
3. Every mechanic and helper in the shops belong to a union.
4. There was a time when you have hurried wherever you went.
5. Everyone at my boarding house are congenial.
6. If you wouldn't have been excited, you wouldn't have put the car in reverse.
7. For contrast, a crude and a refined piece of metal were shown.
8. It was so cold that the water pipes bursted.
9. Max, along with the three other men, is to represent the union at the Milwaukee meeting.
10. *Realms of Gold* are about interesting books for children.
11. If there was less snow, we could back the car out.
12. It has been you and Bob who has carried the heaviest load.
13. If paint would harden in your paint brushes, use varnish remover to dissolve it.
14. Each of the salesmen has promised to help in the drive.
15. The passengers moved back so that others can get on the bus.
16. If he would write more slowly, his writing would be more legible.
17. Can I have one of your extra tickets?
18. Leah, as well as her sister, have good taste in clothes.
19. Everyone expects our team to win.
20. If the blood were from an artery, it would be brighter.
21. To whom will I give the report of the work?

## Practice Test, Verbs

Some of the sentences on this page are incorrect. If a verb is incorrectly used, write the correct form. If a sentence is correct, write C. DO NOT CHANGE ANY SENTENCE THAT IS CORRECT. Do not rewrite the sentence; make the least possible change. Do not change the meaning of the sentence.

On this page consider only verbs.

1. If Miss Smith needs more light, she can use my lamp.
2. For the past three years, the plant is salvaging waste stock.
3. If Mary had of gone to that dance, she would have enjoyed it.
4. Shall we have the living room repapered this spring?
5. If the manager should give the men more responsibility, his problems would disappear.
6. The committee has seen the section foremen last night.
7. Either of the caps fits this bottle.
8. The foreman, as well as the workers, agree that the blueprint is inaccurate.
9. One thing that effects the performance of an engine is the quality of the fuel used.
10. When some of the actors were found unsuitable, the play was recast.
11. So that no epidemic will occur, all were vaccinated.
12. Neither book were the one he wanted.
13. *The Three Musketeers* has been enjoyed by thousands of boys.
14. If the mistake were his fault, he would admit it.
15. A chocolate and a coconut cake is in the box.
16. The saving in postage would have been great if the advertisement had of been printed on lightweight paper.
17. If the Board of Directors would decide to meet today, notify me.
18. He excepted their suggestions with gratitude.
19. Each of the employees punch the time clock twice a day.
20. Joe is the only one of my friends who play bridge well.
21. We walked down the road so that we can see the old fort.

## Pronouns and Possessives

In each of the following sentences there are two or more words or groups of words in parentheses. Only one of these forms is correct. After number 1 on your strip of paper write the correct form for the first sentence. Do this for the other sentences.

Example: There are few men like (he—him). _ _ _ _ _ _ _ _ _ _ _ _ _ _ _ _ _*him*

1. My husband wishes I could sing like (she—her).
2. They believe that it was (I—me) who informed the enemy.
3. Mrs. Dow left us a larger share of her estate than (they—them).
4. I chose the employee (who—whom) I believed was the best trained.
5. The man (who—whom) I took for a farmer was really a bank president.
6. Yes, it was (I—me) who made the investigation.
7. You were cleverer than (me—I) at guessing their intentions.
8. Mr. Harper would like to have more helpers like (he—him).
9. This is the man (who—whom) I think is our best mechanic.
10. I recommended the man (who—whom) I considered best qualified.
11. I have often wished I looked like (she—her).
12. It is (they—them), the disloyal citizens, whom you ought to blame.
13. I have you to thank more than (she—her) for this thoughtful act.
14. A good engineer like (he—him) could improve the process.
15. Was it Judy to (whom—who) you gave the message?
16. Returning to the scene of the accident, he saw a man (who—whom) he was sure had seen what had happened.
17. George hoped it would be (him—he) who would be called upon.
18. The man in (who—whom) you can place your confidence is the man for (whom—who) you should vote.
19. The conductor shook hands with the musician (who—whom) had been soloist.
20. Like (he and I—him and me), the others were assigned to special duties.
21. It was (we—us) who arrived there first, despite our detour.
22. To meet interesting people like (they—them) is refreshing.

# Pronouns and Possessives

For directions and example, see page 55.

1. I saw no one there (which—who) could tell me about the tickets.
2. When there is illness, it is usually (her—she) who is first to help.
3. The forecast promised rain, (which—but) it didn't seem likely.
4. I can't find the girl (who—what) borrowed my dictionary.
5. Too many men like (us—we) had gone into the same business.
6. An electric cord (what—which) is not well insulated is unsafe.
7. (Peter the Great's—Peter's the Great) city is renamed Leningrad.
8. The rider spoke sharply to his horse, (who—which) hesitated and then set off at a gallop.
9. What is the difference between (Tom and Ed's—Tom's and Ed's) cars?
10. The nitrogen (what—which) peas deposit in the soil is taken directly from the air.
11. Mr. Mitchell, (who—whom) you used to know, is to be the new manager.
12. (Kaufman's and Connelly's—Kaufman and Connelly's) play was a box-office success.
13. (John's and Bob's—John and Bob's) expressions were guilty.
14. Here is the (commissioner's of deeds—commissioner of deeds') office.
15. (Brazil's and Peru's—Brazil and Peru's) ambassadors were present.
16. Unlike (she—her), I had had no clerical experience.
17. We met a good-looking and talkative young man, (who—which) turned out to be Marvin's brother.
18. His (son-in-law's—son's-in-law) car was at the curb.
19. Where is the dollar (what—that) your father gave you yesterday?
20. We like to eat at (Parker and Lane's—Parker's and Lane's) new restaurant.
21. The girls (who—whom) I saw in the waiting room are to be hired.
22. (Mother's and daughter's—Mother and daughter's) opinions agreed.

# Reference Section Drill, Pronouns and Possessives

Write the headings *Rule* and *Correct Form* on your strip of paper.

For each sentence refer to your reference section, find the rule that explains the correct usage, and write the number of the rule under the heading *Rule*. Then write the correct form under the heading *Correct Form*.

For this page refer to rules 77b; 81b; 83—84b; 93—94; 101—101b.

1. America needs more men like (he—him).
2. We got into the car, (which—but) we found the battery was dead.
3. This came from the (Chief's of Staff—Chief of Staff's) office.
4. They thought it was (me—I) that you meant.
5. Men serve most loyally the employer (whom—who) they feel understands them and their problems.
6. (Fred and Alice's—Fred's and Alice's) marriage is a happy one.
7. By pulse is meant the beat of blood in an artery, (what—which) can be felt and counted.
8. Wagner was a far greater composer than (he—him).
9. (Husband and wife's—Husband's and wife's) incomes may be reported separately.
10. The only driver (whom—who) I saw on the road wouldn't stop.
11. He watched the girl and the car (who—that) came toward him.
12. He was informed that it was (I—me) who wanted the interview.
13. Do you know any man (who—whom) you think is competent to direct the project?
14. You are more experienced in the stock market than (I—me).
15. Like you and (he—him), I am interested in reducing our costs.
16. I can hardly wait to show you the bargains (what—which) I found.
17. (Walton and Hall's—Walton's and Hall's) annual sale begins today.
18. The man from (who—whom) you bought this desk lamp is going out of business.
19. Everyone wanted to see the pilot and the plane (who—that) had made the rescue.

# Review Test, Verbs, Pronouns, and Possessives

Some of the sentences on this page are incorrect. If a verb, a pronoun, or a possessive is incorrectly used, write the correct form. If a sentence is correct, write C. DO NOT CHANGE ANY SENTENCE THAT IS CORRECT. Do not rewrite any sentence; make the least possible change. Do not change the meaning of the sentence.

1. Clarke, like him, feels that a storm is brewing.
2. I am reading *The Times* for five years.
3. John and Roy's hair needed trimming.
4. If Mr. Jolson were here, he would repair the tire.
5. Belgian police dogs are the kind who will best suit our purpose.
6. Every family in these apartments has telephone service.
7. The orders are in the commander-in-chief's special file.
8. They would have won, if their regular pitcher would of been there.
9. We should be paid more than them because we do a better job.
10. The aldermen, as well as the mayor, hopes for re-election.
11. Will we go to Florida this winter?
12. Someone will be appointed tomorrow, but it will not be she.
13. One of the things what pleased him most was the new work schedule.
14. The five floors of Butler's and Wilcox's store are being remodeled.
15. Do you think I could borrow the typewriter?
16. He would not have needed to buy a new part if he would have oiled the motor regularly.
17. Everyone in the neighborhood admire our cat, Tiger.
18. I should like very much to be an executive like he.
19. Jones is the man whom we know will improve production.
20. I shall walk, so that I can window-shop.
21. If anyone gets that job, it will be me.
22. Isn't that the man for who the reception is being given?
23. If it would snow, the pass would be blocked.
24. It will be he whom I shall ask to plead the case.

# Practice Test, Pronouns and Possessives

Some of the sentences on this page are incorrect. If a pronoun or possessive is incorrectly used, write the correct form. If a sentence is correct, write C. DO NOT CHANGE ANY SENTENCE THAT IS CORRECT. Do not rewrite the sentence; make the least possible change. Do not change the meaning of the sentence.

On this page consider only pronouns and possessives.

1. We have Mr. Hale and Mr. Carr's sales charts here.
2. Frank is the man who I believe will succeed him.
3. I have found my papers. These are them.
4. We want to see the trainer and his seal who appear in the next act.
5. The lecturer, who you may have heard of, is dining with us.
6. He is more discriminating in musical taste than her.
7. The mechanic which worked on my car is a friend of yours.
8. Roger seems able to read much more rapidly than me.
9. In speech and mannerisms Mary is very much like she.
10. This is my father's-in-law office.
11. This road is the one what was resurfaced last year.
12. His brothers, like he, were interested in rural problems.
13. Last night I made a special trip downtown to buy this coat, which I now find that the coat sale is continuing all week.
14. May I present the man to who we are all so deeply indebted?
15. Like you and me, Donald likes to keep up with new developments.
16. Gilbert's and Sullivan's operettas are still very popular.
17. Squirrels and chipmunks' food consists largely of nuts.
18. They assured us that it was us alone who had saved the ship.
19. Forest rangers are men what guard our national parks.
20. Washington and Lee's football team hasn't lost a game this season.
21. The man whom you thought was a customer was really a store detective.
22. Imagine you were me; could you have done better?
23. They attempt to cover a larger territory than us.

## Adjectives and Adverbs

In each of the following sentences there are two or more words or groups of words in parentheses. Only one of these forms is correct. After number 1 on your strip of paper write the correct form for the first sentence. Do this for the other sentences.

Example: We (sure—surely) enjoyed ourselves. _____*surely*

1. Everybody (sure—surely) had a good time at your house.
2. One block was (all the farther—as far as) she could walk.
3. Miss White is a teacher (and—and a) librarian in our school.
4. Frank seems (real—really) serious about going to college.
5. Both the artist (and—and the) copy writer approved of the design.
6. An hour is (all the longer—as long as) the clock will run.
7. I'll (sure—certainly) be glad to hear from you.
8. (Most—Almost) everybody was laughing by that time.
9. It is (some—somewhat) warmer today.
10. Our forces destroyed a submarine (and—and a) battleship.
11. When we heard the noise, we were (real—really) frightened.
12. Forty yards is (all the farther—as far as) I can swim.
13. (Most—Almost) everybody would have done the same.
14. John (sure—surely) enjoyed that football game.
15. The ceiling was (some—somewhat) lighter in color than the walls.
16. Once he was (real—really) convinced, Paul agreed readily.
17. He began his career as a physician (and—and a) surgeon.
18. Anne was (some—somewhat) encouraged by the praise.
19. The night was (real—extremely) dark.
20. It could have happened to (most—almost) anyone.
21. The architect (and—and the) contractor each had separate blueprints.
22. The clerk was (sure—certainly) mistaken about the price.
23. (Most—Almost) all their friends have moved to other cities.
24. The roads were (real—very) dangerous after the snow storm.

## Adjectives and Adverbs

For directions and example, see page 60.

1. There (was—wasn't) but one soldier on guard at the gate.
2. That (sure—certainly) is a remarkable sales record.
3. A quart (and—and a) pint of milk were delivered each morning.
4. The foreman asked what kind (of—of a) tool was wanted.
5. Frank was a better quarterback (than—than a) halfback.
6. I left today's newspaper (somewheres—somewhere) in this room.
7. This is (all the farther—as far as) I am going.
8. He is a better administrator (than—than a) scientist.
9. Use a fat (and—and a) thin man for contrast in your cartoon.
10. A painter (and—and a) decorator was calcimining the walls.
11. We can print any kind (of—of a) letterhead for you.
12. It was (kind of—rather) late when I returned.
13. Mrs. Todd claims that she is a better cook (than—than a) chef.
14. Mrs. Van Allen employs both a governess (and—and a) nurse.
15. Joe's first day at work seemed (sort of—rather) long.
16. I (had—hadn't) hardly finished when the whistle blew.
17. Tom is a more successful broadcaster (than—than a) technician.
18. The community will present some kind (of—of a) play this year.
19. Bill was a (real—very) good mechanic.
20. Each member of the group carried a light (and—and a) heavy pack.
21. The ring was (nowhere—nowheres) to be found.
22. She is a better typist (than—than a) bookkeeper.
23. The criticism was (sort of—somewhat) hard to accept.
24. The shop is (somewheres—somewhere) near the post office.
25. The men (hardly—don't hardly) know what to do next.
26. The building would make a better home (than—than an) office.
27. (Most—Almost) all the members present favored the motion.

# Review Test, Verbs, Pronouns, Possessives, Adjectives, and Adverbs

For directions, see page 53.

On this page consider verbs, pronouns, possessives, adjectives, and adverbs.

1. Elizabeth was real sincere in her apologies.
2. Ted, as well as his fellow workers, are confident of success.
3. Any kind of a ledger will do, but this kind is very serviceable.
4. I believe it was her who drew up the petition.
5. If he chooses one of us, I think his choice will be you rather than I.
6. The new paint hadn't scarcely dried before it rained.
7. The young and old people suffered greatly during the famine.
8. I know we could meet that deadline if Davis were here.
9. Mr. Peel, who the shipment was intended for, will not accept it.
10. The small amount collected disappointed the committee some.
11. The hill was kind of steep for an old man to climb.
12. Will we meet you at six, or after dinner?
13. The note is due today, which we regret that we cannot renew it.
14. He has compared Jack's and Bill's records.
15. A round and a square table was exhibited in the shop window.
16. The secretary and treasurer arrived.   Together they examined the auditor's report.
17. John had most recovered from his broken arm when he broke his leg.
18. I asked for Barry, who I knew had a good command of French.
19. The Chief's of Maintenance staff works here.
20. Neither of us think the play is good enough to succeed.
21. This is Smug, our English bulldog, who is an important member of the household.
22. Mr. Fielding seems to make a better repairman than a salesman.
23. The old man which I talked to is the owner of the shop.

## Prepositions

In each of the following sentences there are two or more words or groups of words in parentheses. Only one of these forms is correct. After number 1 on your strip of paper write the correct form for the first sentence. Do this for the other sentences.

Example: The cat (wants in—wants to come in)._____*wants to come in*

1. Rags scratches at the door when he (wants to come in—wants in).
2. The storm blew the roof (off—off of) the house.
3. (Beside—Besides) taking his dictation, she handles routine mail.
4. Her father doesn't (like—like for) her to read so much because her eyesight is poor.
5. Do you (remember—remember of) making triplicate copies of that invoice?
6. Frank jumped (off—off of) the wagon and picked up the pitchfork which had fallen to the ground.
7. Sally (wants—wants for) him to do the stenciling this time.
8. (Besides—Beside) delivering papers, he works in a drug store.
9. I can't (remember—remember of) ever having seen her before.
10. He doesn't (like for—like) you to take the risk.
11. Father didn't (recollect—recollect of) having paid the bill.
12. (Besides—Beside) the chair was a brightly lighted lamp.
13. The folder you took (off—off of) the desk was Betty's.
14. Ralph was cold and said he (wanted in—wanted to come in).
15. The warden (wants—wants for) to see the man at once.
16. Strangers picked all the fruit (off—off of) the trees.
17. Jerry couldn't (recall—recall of) having made the statement which was printed in the papers.
18. When the rain stopped, the children (wanted out—wanted to go out).
19. (Besides—Beside) writing the book, he illustrated it.
20. I (want—want for) him to go to college if he can.
21. He may (remember—remember of) having recommended Miss Ward.

## Prepositions

For directions and example, see page 63.

1. (Besides—Beside) getting the bonus, he received a promotion.
2. Lola and Ed were accompanied to the train (with—by) their friends.
3. The banquet was followed (by—with) a number of witty speeches.
4. I wish I could (recollect—recollect of) where I met her.
5. The ship was built (within—inside of) four weeks.
6. Poverty is often accompanied (with—by) broken homes, bad housing, and ill health.
7. Every two hours of hard work was followed (with—by) a rest period.
8. This button came (off—off of) General Grant's coat.
9. (Besides—Beside) your railroad ticket, you must pay for a Pullman seat.
10. The family will all be here (within—inside of) ten minutes.
11. The new serum was credited with preventing many patients from dying (with—of) pneumonia.
12. The episode was followed (with—by) tears and reproaches.
13. The neighbors would (like—like for) us to turn off the radio.
14. The storm was accompanied (with—by) wind and sleet.
15. The council differed (with—from) the mayor on that issue.
16. Because of vaccination and sanitation, very few people in the United States die (of—with) smallpox.
17. He does not differ (from—with) you in theory, but he will not do what you suggest.
18. The coroner's jury said the victim died (with—of) exposure.
19. Bess (wanted off—wanted to get off) at the eleventh floor.
20. Jack's disposition differs (from—with) that of his father.
21. The mayor was accompanied to the scene (with—by) motor police.
22. Dessert was followed (with—by) mints and nuts.
23. (Within—Inside of) an hour, the jury returned a verdict.

# Review Test, Verbs, Pronouns, Possessives, Adjectives, Adverbs, and Prepositions

For directions, see page 53.

On this page consider verbs, pronouns, possessives, adjectives, adverbs, and prepositions.

1. I told her that she could use my desk while I was on vacation.
2. I am better satisfied than him with the results.
3. He said Corot was a better landscape artist than a portrait painter.
4. Miss Tilden doesn't recall of having made such an appointment for me.
5. He demonstrated with a pure and adulterated sample.
6. Carey, who I worked with in Washington, has been transferred.
7. A green and a yellow sweater is still to be packed.
8. The commissioner's assistant was real gracious to us.
9. The top fell off of the box and a snake was revealed.
10. Beside the main store we have three suburban branches.
11. More people die with heart disease than from any other cause.
12. This department, along with two others, are trying the new system.
13. Either of the methods were acceptable to the statistician.
14. Every crack and crevice in these walls have been filled with putty.
15. Mabel asked for to work with Jean this afternoon.
16. Put your bag down anywheres that you can find room.
17. The statement was accompanied with reservations on my part.
18. The increase in salary was a better reward than bonus.
19. If the highway was better lighted, night driving would be safer.
20. Where is the man who you said was so interested in photography?
21. Inside of ten years, public opinion changed completely.
22. Mr. Smith makes some kind of a motor in his factory.
23. Dorothy remembered of seeing Cornell in *The Three Sisters*.
24. My handwriting is not very different than yours.

# Conjunctions

In each of the following sentences there are two or more words or groups of words in parentheses. Only one of these forms is correct. After number 1 on your strip of paper, write the correct form for the first sentence. Do this for the other sentences.

Example: We are interested in your proposal, (and—but) we
cannot take advantage of it. _____*but*

1. Fred went to meet his father, (and—but) he missed him somehow.
2. (Without—Unless) you keep your things in order, you can't find them easily when you want them.
3. I don't know (as—that) I care to vote for Graham.
4. Why don't you come to see us, (like—as) you promised?
5. We read (where—that) stocks had fallen and fortunes had been lost.
6. Everything was in readiness for his coming, (except—except that) the welcoming committee had not arrived.
7. We must rate them (as—like) we learned in the instructors' course.
8. Maude says it seems (as though—like) her work is never finished.
9. I read (where—that) more men would be needed to finish the job.
10. Carr's charts were helpful (except—except that) they were complicated.
11. He should fulfill the terms of the contract (like—as) he agreed to do.
12. The coat fits Gordon very well (except—except that) the sleeves are a little too short.
13. Has that procedure been changed (like—as) we suggested?
14. Betty read in the papers (that—where) Charles had become a hero.
15. Jim made the drawing (as—like) the superintendent directed.
16. Lois promised to wait for Mary, (and—but) she forgot.
17. You will not be put on night work (except—unless) you volunteer.
18. I don't know (as—that) I like our new hours.
19. She hesitated (like—as though) she felt the price was too high.
20. Madge won't accept the invitation (without—unless) you are invited too.

## Conjunctions

For directions and example, see page 66.

1. Ted missed your call tonight (on account of—because) he was not at home.
2. He seemed well enough (except—except that) he refused to eat.
3. I do not want either arguments (nor—or) excuses.
4. (That—Because) Roy did not come did not mean that he was ill.
5. I don't know (as—that) you can find better service anywhere.
6. Neither pencil (or—nor) ink will do; use a typewriter.
7. The reason for my return is (that—because) I forgot my keys.
8. The radio whistled (on account of—because) a tube was loose.
9. (That—Because) you didn't know the rules won't be a sufficient excuse for your failure to report.
10. The applicant was suitable (except—except that) he was under age.
11. Don't send either stamps (or—nor) personal check with the order.
12. The reason for his hesitancy was (because—that) he disliked to blame anyone without proof.
13. Neither glue (or—nor) mucilage would hold it, but rubber cement worked very well.
14. Polly had not read more than a chapter (until—when) quivers began to run up and down her spine.
15. He enjoyed neither Bach (nor—or) Beethoven so much as Mozart.
16. You didn't act (like—as if) you were pleased about it.
17. (That—Because) the roof leaked was our principal objection.
18. The program was a great success (on account of—because) every parent thought his child performed well.
19. Grant had hardly started to dictate (than—when) the telephone rang.
20. The reason she cried was (because—that) she was sorry for the heroine.
21. The day was fine (except—except that) it was a little cold.

## Reference Section Drill, Adjectives, Adverbs, Prepositions, and Conjunctions

Write the headings *Rule* and *Correct Form* on your strip of paper.

For each sentence refer to your reference section, find the rule that explains the correct usage, and write the number of the rule under the heading *Rule*. Then write the correct form under the heading *Correct Form*.

For this page refer to rules 112—115; 121; 125; 126—127; 128—129; 133a—135; 140; 142—143; 145; 155—156; 158; 160—162; 164b—171a; 173—173a; 176.

1. Are you (real—really) sure they have the pliers in stock?
2. I don't (recall—recall of) having seen him before.
3. (Sure—Surely) you can get your work done on time.
4. Howard laughed (like—as if) he enjoyed the story.
5. (Within—Inside of) thirty minutes, he had found the error.
6. The book was a best seller, (and—but) it was poorly written.
7. They advertised for a cook (and—and a) gardener.
8. Would he like (to see—for to see) my pictures of the lake?
9. Have you (most—almost) finished reading that report?
10. He wrote a true (and—and a) false statement about each subject.
11. Neither man (or—nor) beast could live in the desolate place.
12. The regular program was followed (by—with) five encores.
13. Always keep some sort (of—of an) antiseptic in the medicine cabinet.
14. Nobody thought (as—that) he would dare to make the trip.
15. That enlargement differs in quality (from—with) this contact print.
16. It was a (kind of—rather) friendly thing for a busy man to do.
17. The box (was—was not) hardly big enough, but he used it.
18. Did he die (of—with) blood poisoning?
19. Isn't there a tearoom (somewheres—somewhere) near here?
20. The house was excellent (except—except that) it needed painting.
21. The reason we won was (because—that) we had the better team.
22. (On account of—Because) the majority favored it, the bill passed.

# Practice Test, Adjectives, Adverbs, Prepositions, and Conjunctions

Some of the sentences on this page are incorrect.  If an adjective, adverb, preposition, or conjunction is incorrectly used, write the correct form.  If a sentence is correct, write C.  DO NOT CHANGE ANY SENTENCE THAT IS CORRECT.  Do not rewrite the sentence; make the least possible change.  Do not change the meaning of the sentence.

1. The Chief Justice died with pneumonia after a brief illness.
2. Anyone who wants in must have an official pass.
3. The man looked like he had been very ill.
4. The bill was correct except the date was omitted.
5. This item in the paper should be real interesting to you.
6. We need two men, a chemistry teacher and athletic coach.
7. Beside being delicious, oranges are rich in vitamin C.
8. "He sure was anxious to receive the shipment without delay," Dick said.
9. Not for a minute did either the rain slacken or the wind cease.
10. Jim won't get his raise without he works hard.
11. The new and used copy of his manuscript lay on the desk.
12. I can't recall, even faintly, of having seen the original bill.
13. This looks some like the sample she sent in to be matched.
14. She is a better talker than a listener.
15. Would Mr. Russell like for me to retype that letter?
16. He will be here inside of a month.
17. The first years of struggle were followed by a period of prosperity.
18. They would be as willing to hire a woman as man for this job.
19. The reason he ran was because the train was leaving.
20. Usually he dictates his letters, and occasionally he writes in longhand.
21. The typist and stenographer have taken a course in business English.
22. He had hardly completed the training than he was promoted.
23. "I beg to differ from you on that point," he objected.
24. I don't see where anyone was to blame for the fire.

# Punctuation

Some of the sentences on this page are incorrectly punctuated. If a punctuation mark has been omitted or incorrectly used, indicate the correct punctuation, as shown in the sample. If a sentence is correct, write C. DO NOT CHANGE ANY SENTENCE THAT IS CORRECT.

Example: It would be he warned very difficult. ____*be, he warned, very*

1. The plan we thought was the best that could be adopted.
2. More than four hundred property owners were present and each of them protested against the action of the tax commission.
3. A long narrow winding road led from the house to the village.
4. After health examinations for school children were inaugurated their health improved somewhat.
5. He would never find he felt sure a more loyal friend.
6. The new president of the club was George Brewster the vice president of the year before.
7. Since the man was blind he depended largely on his faithful dog for guidance.
8. Ross had forestalled, he fondly believed, that very emergency.
9. There are more than twenty raw materials which an industrial nation must have and yet no nation can obtain all twenty from its own possessions.
10. Tom rode in on a limping black horse.
11. The ring a narrow circlet set with diamonds lay winking in the sun.
12. When the pan used on an electric range is wide enough to cover the heating unit waste of heat is avoided.
13. Red, white, and blue ribbons streamed from the bouquet.
14. Mr. Lewis the radio commentator explained the system clearly.
15. Four clerks he estimated could complete the indexing.
16. Since the elevator was out of order, we came up the stairs.
17. Whose is this smooth legible handwriting?

## Punctuation

For directions and example, see page 70.

1. John Masefield's poem, Sea Fever, describes a sailor's yearning for the sea.

2. His serious, young face showed how much the interview meant to him.

3. "Davis said, Return it to stock, but it was too badly damaged," the clerk reported.

4. We have the following supplies: 500 white file cards, one quire of bond paper, 13 boxes of paper clips.

5. A family should not spend according to some authorities more than twenty per cent of its income for rent.

6. "She said, I like skating, and I said, So do I, and then we were friends," Madge replied.

7. A man who had witnessed the accident, was soon found.

8. Among her duties are these, filing, typing, stencil cutting, and answering the telephone.

9. I enjoyed Lamb's Essay on Roast Pig more than any other of his essays.

10. The purpose of the ruse was, to get John out of danger.

11. Next month he decided would be the time to plow and plant the field.

12. The director introduced Mann his new assistant.

13. The jostling crowds and the heavy traffic, made progress slow.

14. "I said, "You are always so clumsy," and then I wished I had not said it," Mrs. Hodges confessed.

15. The heirs of the deceased are as follows Rose White Sylvia Thompson James Ingles and Mary Ingles.

16. A long line of depositors, stood at the cashier's window.

17. The following firms sent bids by air mail, Smith and Peters, Wells and Company, and Arlen Associates.

18. He wanted to know, whether everything possible had been done.

# Review Test, Conjunctions and Punctuation

For directions and examples, see pages 69 and 70.

On this page consider only conjunctions and punctuation.

1. They sat down on the shady green lawn under a wide oak.
2. The bulletin says where a new date has been set for the hearing.
3. The movie a Western of the wildest sort delighted Bill.
4. The reason that he bought the collection of old books was because it was such a bargain.
5. It would be possible he conceded to start at once if we were ready.
6. The best features of this poster are, its timeliness, its striking composition, and its universal appeal.
7. We shall be glad to have you address the club at our April meeting and you are also invited to the luncheon which follows.
8. Many who heard the new phonograph record, wanted to buy it.
9. I don't know as he is the most suitable one for the job.
10. Flickering interlacing shadows mottled the pool.
11. That he does not like fighting does not mean that he will allow anyone to bully him.
12. When he has visitors don't interrupt him unless it is unavoidable.
13. It began to look like the book would be a best seller.
14. The following foods were rationed early in 1943 canned fruits and vegetables meat butter and cheese.
15. The magazine, the newspaper, and the book, substantiated his claim.
16. The piano accompaniment was neither intricate or difficult.
17. He could not escape punishment without he told a lie.
18. The weapon an automatic pistol was found under the porch.
19. Mrs. Rogers stated with emphasis, "He said to me, I'll be back at nine, and I am sure he will."
20. The stock clerk could not find either the pencils nor the stamps.

## Sentence Structure

Some of the groups of words on this page contain errors in sentence structure. Write the correct form on your strip of paper as indicated in the sample. If a sentence is correct, write C. DO NOT CHANGE ANY SENTENCE THAT IS CORRECT.

Example: This summer I may travel and summer is my
favorite season. ----------------------*travel. Summer*

1. Charlie started on his job in July and he had never worked before.
2. Miss Spencer was the new office manager. She was experienced. She was efficient and courteous.
3. Running through the woods, a signal from a flashlight made John halt quickly.
4. The parts should not be packed in the boxes unless they are painted.
5. Having made the drawing, the next undertaking for Bill was the blueprint.
6. The box was lying on the table. It was made of polished wood. It had an elaborately engraved lid.
7. Coming up the steps, the package beside the door was seen by Susan.
8. Jeanne is a good violinist, but she wants to play it better.
9. Inspecting the roof, a large rusty hole was found which had to be repaired.
10. The cream separator was out of order again and it never did work very well.
11. Having carefully checked the list, she returned it for correction.
12. Jerry wrote an order for the supplies. He attached a check to it. He put it into an envelope and mailed it.
13. Being very hungry, the sandwich tasted unusually good to Jack.
14. Our car needs new piston rings and it has traveled sixty thousand miles.
15. Without hurrying, the machine was installed by the workmen in less than an hour.
16. Fred's toothache hurt him so much that he had it pulled.

## Sentence Structure

For directions and example, see page 73.

1. I told her when she came in to get a receipt.

2. Moore has become an expert photographer since he started working in it.

3. Shadow pictures are when you throw on the wall shadows of the fingers in various positions.

4. The alarm had not gone off and Ray must have forgotten to set it.

5. Bob was using a new movie projector which he had bought it on approval.

6. When making a cake, the flour should be sifted thoroughly.

7. Miss Fenton said that her accounts would not balance and the head of the department helped her with them.

8. When typed, send the report to Mr. Graham.

9. Grace said the plan would not work beforehand.

10. While standing in the aisle, the train started unexpectedly and threw me into an old gentleman's lap.

11. The iodine test for starch is where a weak solution of iodine is used, which turns blue if starch is present.

12. The box contained thirteen doughnuts, which the proprietor called them a baker's dozen.

13. Mr. Smith advised Mary when she applied for the job to be punctual.

14. I think that the police have made an arrest but they have arrested the wrong man.

15. While shopping, an unusual bargain in hats tempted me.

16. It was a large book. It was red. It had fine print and narrow margins.

17. To keep insects from damaging your garden chairs paint their legs with creosote.

18. When painted, allow the surface to dry thoroughly.

19. Margaret asked me on the way home to buy some bread.

## Sentence Structure

For directions and example, see page 73.

1. The applicant said he was an expert typist, accountant, and could write advertising copy.

2. When you speculate in the stock market, a person should be prepared to lose money as well as to win it.

3. Although patched in several places, Foster thought he could use the tire.

4. The pudding was made of milk, eggs, bread, baked in the oven, and served cold.

5. William thinks and talks slowly. He is usually right in his decisions.

6. Arthur had such a severe cold that he was undecided whether to go to work or he should remain at home.

7. We first built a fire; we then heated soup, vegetables, and made coffee.

8. He cut the board to the necessary length, then planed it, and finally it was sanded by him.

9. As a student nurse, she learned to take temperatures, make beds, and doing countless other tasks.

10. Mr. Carlisle not only wanted more men for the highway job but more tools and materials as well.

11. He promised that he would come and that he would take the job.

12. Trigonometry seems logical and easy enough. I never could learn it.

13. Steel posts, handrails, fences, brass knobs, and aluminum bowls were replaced by wooden ones.

14. Marcel had had opportunity neither to learn correct English nor of practicing it.

15. I should have washed the car that Saturday. I weeded the garden.

16. To calibrate is when you standardize an instrument of measurement.

17. Sally seems to make mistakes in everything that is done by her.

# Review Test, Conjunctions, Punctuation, and Sentence Structure

Some of the sentences on this page contain errors in conjunctions, punctuation, or sentence structure. If a sentence is correct, write C. DO NOT CHANGE ANY SENTENCE THAT IS CORRECT. If a sentence is incorrect, make the least possible change that will correct it. Do not change the meaning of any sentence.

1. He wrote rapidly and carelessly, like he read.
2. Beautiful lofty slender pines covered the sides of the mountain.
3. Peter was telling us about his life in the Army and he looks well.
4. Anne told us that Tom was at home when she left but he was not there when she returned.
5. The newspapers said, that the new reform candidate was honest.
6. We heard where Jean had been promoted.
7. At five, Janet could read, write, and sing a number of songs.
8. Because the ashes were still warm indicated the recent presence of an intruder in the cabin.
9. Before he started on the trip, Ted knew that the car needed repair.
10. His judgment he asserted had been excellent in his youth.
11. Flashing brilliantly in the darkness, the villagers were terrified by flares from the distressed ship.
12. What pleases me most is, that a salary increase goes with the job.
13. While at home, a telephone call informed me I should report for work.
14. Funeral in Eden, by Paul Maguire, is a good mystery story.
15. Powers said that they could either meet in your office or in his.
16. It seems he always calls after you will be on the way home.
17. "Peters will say, "I told you so," if I lose money on this investment," said Frank.
18. We opened the boxes which the saleswoman had wrapped them in tissue and tied with ribbons.
19. Jones gave us specific directions on what to take with us and where we should report.

## Practice Test, Punctuation and Sentence Structure

For directions and examples, see pages 70 and 73.

1. The factory was well lighted. It was well ventilated. It had many safety devices to protect the workers.

2. If Jack had heard the remark he made no outward sign.

3. Running and with a shout, he reached the bus before it left the curb.

4. "He said, "The valves need grinding," but I knew I couldn't afford that, so I drove away," Bill said.

5. Using her typewriter, a long letter was written before Ethel went to bed.

6. A subpoena is when a person is ordered to appear as a witness in court.

7. Every man possessing the necessary skills, was urged to volunteer.

8. All you good citizens should cast your ballots early tomorrow.

9. No boy should miss reading The Adventures of Tom Sawyer.

10. If unable to report for duty, a message should be sent to that effect.

11. At the ball park the boys devoured peanuts, popcorn, candy, and annoyed people sitting near them.

12. The guard asked him when he came in to show his pass.

13. The smoke he believed was coming from the woods five miles away.

14. Your work shows, that you have skillful hands and a good eye.

15. We hope that Bob will be successful in the new job and he will like living in Colorado.

16. I studied not only the assignment, but took notes on it, too.

17. All his newspapers were two days old. I bought one.

18. A tree blocked the highway, and we should have taken the other road.

19. Some of the men were unable to finish the work in the time allotted and some of them refused to work until wages were increased.

20. Looking from my window, the clock in the steeple can be clearly seen.

## Cumulative Review, Part Two

If there is a mistake in the first line, write the correct form on your strip of paper. Then write the correct forms for the other lines. If any line does not contain a mistake, write C. If there are two errors in any line, correct both. DO NOT CHANGE ANY LINE THAT IS CORRECT.

Mr. Horace Drake
Sawyer and Drake, Wholesale Chemists
1189 South Boulevard
New City, Ohio

Dear Mr. Drake:

1. Our firm shall be greatly pleased to assist you in designing, lay-
2. ing out, and to illustrate the advertising booklet you have in mind.
3. Your partner, Mr. Sawyer, has made some excellent general notes,
4. if it was him who wrote them. However, if he does not mind I wish to
5. differ from him on the matter of photographs. The reason I object to
6. photographs in this type of advertising booklet is, because they limit
7. the choice of paper. If not used, line cuts can be employed and will
8. be every bit as effective. Please tell Mr. Sawyer, whom I believe will
9. consider my viewpoint carefully, to be the judge in this matter.
10. You will I feel sure wish to save the center pages for the regional
11. map, so that the latter would not be broken at the fold. Your suggested
12. line drawing of Sawyer's and Drake's trade-mark, should make an at-
13. tractive cover design. The order form and back cover might be printed
14. in fairly small type. Examining the copy, these pages seemed to me
15. to be sort of crowded.
16. Probably ten persons look at the illustrations for every one who look
17. at the text. For this reason, each illustration should be self-explana-
18. tory. Unless clear simple sketches and charts are used, neither type of
19. illustration are likely to be effective. You will therefore feel, like we
20. do, that the illustrations need further discussion. Can I see you on
21. Wednesday to talk over the details?

            Yours truly,

            John Grey

# PART THREE

## Verbs

In each of the following sentences there are two or more words or groups of words in parentheses. Only one of these forms is correct. After number 1 on your strip of paper write the correct form for the first sentence. Do this for the other sentences.

Example: Either men or boys (was—were) wanted. _____*were*

1. Madge or Dorothy (is—are) to take charge of the reservations.
2. Mrs. Gates will (lend—loan) us her punch bowl for the party.
3. He (brought—took) his tools there when he started the job.
4. After the play had ended, the cast (was—were) invited to repeat the performance the following week.
5. Either dye or oil paints (is—are) used to color cloth.
6. Should the United States (lend—loan) more money to the little nations?
7. When you go downstairs, (take—bring) this report to Mr. Woods.
8. Neither the driver nor the horses (was—were) hurt.
9. He intends to (take—bring) his family from here to Omaha.
10. The union (have—has) voted to accept the terms.
11. Either picric acid gauze or tannic acid solution (is—are) used for treating burns.
12. Whether the Army or the Navy (do—does) it, it should be done soon.
13. Please (lend—loan) me your dictionary for a moment.
14. Our family (has—have) agreed not to exchange gifts this year.
15. Either the employer or his workers (decide—decides) the policy.
16. Neither the morning edition nor the night edition (was—were) on time.
17. Please (bring—take) a newspaper with you when you come.
18. The first-aid class (is—are) practicing bandaging one another.
19. Neither the envelopes nor the stamps (is—are) what we asked for.
20. If either Harry or John (find—finds) it, the kit will be returned.
21. Manning will (lend—loan) us the long-carriage typewriter from his office.

## Verbs

For directions and example, see page 79.

1. Plenty of fruits, eggs, and vegetables (is—are) needed for health.
2. Aeronautics (have—has) advanced rapidly in the last decade.
3. The owner and inventor of the patent (are—is) John C. Reynolds.
4. Miss Fay explained that not all bacteria (are—were) harmful.
5. The huge tongs (encircles—encircle) the box as the crane turns.
6. News from home (was—were) what he asked for first.
7. A block and tackle (is—are) needed to lift that heavy machine.
8. Over four fifths of the building (was—were) completed in one month.
9. Three weeks with pay (is—are) allowed each employee.
10. The refugees' thanks (was—were) fervently expressed.
11. Civics (include—includes) the study of the rights and duties of citizens.
12. The agricultural agent said that the boll weevil (is—was) one of the most destructive insect pests.
13. Ten hours (is—are) enough time to spend writing that paper.
14. Plenty of hard work (accompanies—accompany) the process.
15. The founder and editor of the magazine you are reading (is—are) occupying seat 7 on this plane.
16. He was glad he (primed—had primed) the new wood before painting.
17. Riches (do—does) not compensate for poor health.
18. After he (painted—had painted) the screens, he put them away.
19. Mathematics (deal—deals) with quantitative measurement.
20. Hertz proved that electromagnetic waves (are—were) transmitted through space with the speed of light.
21. A jail term and fine of $1000 (is—are) the usual penalty.
22. Roy made the sale after he (tried—had tried) twice in vain.
23. A number of the plants in this row (have—has) been weeded out.

## Verbs

For directions and example, see page 79.

1. The clock (will—shall) probably run if you oil it.
2. I (have—have been) and shall continue to be grateful.
3. I promise that I (shall—will) deliver the goods early.
4. She would have been ready (to drop—to have dropped) everything.
5. I (should—would) like to see that play.
6. Mr. Abbott (has—has got) to wait for authorization from Washington.
7. I (shall—will) need a student lamp for my desk.
8. Alec would have liked (to have met—to meet) you.
9. The rain will soak him if it has (not—not soaked him) already.
10. The commandant has ordered that no one (shall—will) leave the post.
11. Our catalog (shall—will) be issued during the first week in March.
12. Wire us if you (do not have—have not got) these items in stock.
13. I know that if he had time he (would—should) recheck the figures.
14. Jim would have been ready (to have interpreted—to interpret) the catcher's signals if he had been concentrating on the game.
15. His father is determined that Jack (shall—will) make the trip with him.
16. Captain Coles (got—was) cited for extraordinary heroism.
17. I was determined that I (should—would) deny their request.
18. When your messenger (got—was) hurt, our company doctor treated him.
19. The tax bill (shall—will) probably be debated next week.
20. He would have preferred to (have been—be) in America this year.
21. He has said before and (will—will say) again that he does not believe the charge.
22. Howard agreed that the plan (would—should) not be feasible.
23. You may say what you like, but (I will—shall) never agree.
24. This machine never (has—has worked) and never will work so well as the other.

# Reference Section Drill, Verbs

Write the headings *Rule* and *Correct Form* on your strip of paper.

For each sentence refer to your reference section, find the rule that explains the correct usage, and write the number of the rule under the heading *Rule*. Then write the correct form under the heading *Correct Form*.

For this page refer to rules 34—35; 41—41a; 43—44; 46—49; 52—53; 62—62a; 62c—63; 65—66.

1. Ten minutes (seems—seem) an hour when one is waiting for a phone call.

2. Explorers found that the Amazon (was—is) the world's longest river.

3. A bright spring morning or a cool autumn evening (seem—seems) always to improve my disposition.

4. I went there last year and (shall—shall go) again when I can.

5. The bakery and restaurant on the southeast corner of Howard Square (have—has) excellent food.

6. Robert was sure that they (should—would) be glad to help.

7. They (took—brought) me to the hospital, but I was sent home after treatment.

8. The committee (was—were) told how the funds had been employed.

9. After dinner I (will—shall) probably read awhile.

10. Neither washing soda nor harsh laundry soaps (is—are) safe for laundering these stockings.

11. (Have you—Have you got) time to stop for me on your way to work?

12. The scissors (was—were) sharpened by cutting a piece of sandpaper.

13. The variety of tasks performed by Mr. Brown (was—were) remarkable.

14. You (shall—will) not undergo such a risk for any cause.

15. Her iron did not heat because she (damaged—had damaged) the terminals.

16. Gentlemen, we ask you to (lend—loan) this small sum, not to give it.

17. Shingles (is—are) caused by a virus which attacks the nerves.

18. I should have liked to (have read—read) the book last night.

19. Mr. West was determined that his old friend (should—would) be seated at the speaker's table.

## Practice Test, Verbs

Some of the sentences on this page are incorrect. If a verb is incorrectly used, write the correct form. If a sentence is correct, write C. DO NOT CHANGE ANY SENTENCE THAT IS CORRECT. Do not rewrite the sentence; make the least possible change. Do not change the meaning of the sentence.

On this page consider only verbs.

1. The home economics class invite you to lunch on Monday.
2. After the farmer drained the swamp, the mosquitoes disappeared.
3. Six got reprimanded by the judge for the disorder.
4. Neither the storm nor the lightning flashes seem to disturb him.
5. The mechanic said that the best place for a thermostat was away from doors and windows.
6. Mr. Moore would have known what to have said to him.
7. Neither Wendell nor he were interested in the offer.
8. Two miles a day are as much as you had better walk at first.
9. Mr. Brown was determined that his children would learn to swim.
10. Please loan me your eraser for a moment.
11. The coat was long enough, but the trousers was too short.
12. I have driven carefully and will all my life.
13. Bring your birth certificate when you go.
14. Physics were the subject radio technicians had to master.
15. I promise that I shall never sell the farm.
16. Six months are the usual guarantee period for these machines.
17. The rope and pulley is valuable for lifting heavy loads.
18. Kate would have volunteered to have got the water.
19. The rest of the woods was not searched.
20. Jones shall probably make this survey, and I will make the other.
21. Either Jane or Sue usually answer the telephone.
22. The team was awarded their letters in June.
23. I did not know that the Senate had ninety-six members.

# Pronouns and Possessives

In each of the following sentences there are two or more words or groups of words in parentheses. Only one of these forms is correct. After number 1 on your strip of paper write the correct form for the first sentence. Do this for the other sentences.

Example: (Whoever—Whomever) else goes, he won't. _____*Whoever*

1. Tell (whoever—whomever) answers the phone that the road is blocked.
2. (Whomever—Whoever) the car hit was badly injured.
3. He was surprised when he found the new neighbors to be (them—they).
4. Give the money to (whoever—whomever) you think needs it.
5. I suspected the culprit to be (he—him).
6. We believe (whoever—whomever) found the book will return it.
7. (Who—Whom) do you think would object to the plan?
8. We must prevent (whoever—whomever) did this from trying again.
9. Most of the people expected the successful candidate to be (he—him).
10. Nobody here remembered to bring (his—their) compass.
11. (Who—Whom) do the police intend to arrest?
12. I will appoint (whoever—whomever) the group chooses.
13. The Martins are grateful to (whoever—whomever) reported the fire.
14. Did you understand it to be (he—him) that the captain praised?
15. Grimes always scowled at (whoever—whomever) walked on his lawn.
16. (Who—Whom) did the neighbors charge with the mischief?
17. (Whoever—Whomever) you select will be satisfactory to me.
18. Anyone with imagination and a few materials can make (their—his) own greeting cards.
19. We thank (whoever—whomever) made the suggestion.
20. I knew it to be (she—her) when I answered the telephone.
21. The sentry challenged (whoever—whomever) he saw approaching the gate.
22. Unless I knew otherwise, I should never have thought the author to be (he—him).

## Pronouns and Possessives

For directions and example, see page 84.

1. There were four hunters and each had (his—their) dog.
2. Every supervisor has given efficiency ratings to (their—his) employees.
3. The association will hold (its—their) convention in St. Louis.
4. One's shoes should fit (them—him) properly.
5. If (their—his) parentage is unknown, anyone who is under age and lives in the United States is considered a citizen.
6. Mrs. Kane or Helen forgot (their—her) umbrella last night.
7. Neither machine was operating at (its—their) full speed.
8. One should visit (his—their) dentist once or twice each year.
9. Neither of the two remembered (his—their) own promise.
10. Neither device brought (its—their) inventor fame or money.
11. One may put in (his—your) application any time next week.
12. Philip or Henry wrote but forgot to sign (his—their) name.
13. Everybody had been told that (they—he) must report to the foreman.
14. When the group finished eating, (it—they) cleared away all traces of the picnic.
15. Everybody should mix (their—his) paints carefully and slowly.
16. The regiment advanced steadily, (their—its) flags fluttering in the breeze.
17. A workman or a visitor may have (their—his) lunch here.
18. Our community will try to lower (their—its) accident rate.
19. Each store tried to undersell (its—their) competitors.
20. The team left the field wearily, and (its—their) shoulders drooped dejectedly.
21. One often finds (their—his) pen running dry in the middle of a page.
22. Every line in the story reflects (their—its) author's personality.
23. The coach urged everyone to keep (his—their) eyes on the ball.

## Pronouns and Possessives

For directions and example, see page 84.

1. Do your father and (you—yourself) operate the business?
2. The (house's windows—windows of the house) were broken.
3. This must be (someone's else—someone else's) bicycle.
4. (It says in this notice—This notice says) that the motor operates on alternating current.
5. Mr. Oliver says that his wife and (he—himself) think sensible diets better than doctors' bills.
6. (A storage battery's plates—The plates of a storage battery) are made of lead alloy.
7. (The article says—It says in the article) that veneer is a layer of expensive wood covering cheaper material.
8. (They make the best clothes chests—The best clothes chests are made) of cedar.
9. (He—His) not being a citizen meant that he could not vote.
10. (It told on that radio program—That radio program told) how to choose good lubricating oils.
11. Your comments are constructive, and we shall be glad to act on (the same—them).
12. The accountant and (I—myself) went over the financial statement item by item.
13. It is (nobody else's—nobody's else) fault but mine.
14. I was happy about (you—your) getting the promotion.
15. The secretary read the minutes, and the club voted to accept (them—the same).
16. At home (they called him—he was called) by his middle name.
17. (Him—His) rising from the chair showed that the interview had ended.
18. (Anyone's else—Anyone else's) absence would have been noticed.

## Reference Section Drill, Pronouns and Possessives

Write the headings *Rule* and *Correct Form* on your strip of paper.

For each sentence refer to your reference section, find the rule that explains the correct usage, and write the number of the rule under the heading *Rule*. Then write the correct form under the heading *Correct Form*.

For this page refer to rules 84c—84d; 85—86; 88—92; 96a—99; 102a—104.

1. (Who—Whom) did you think the murderer was?
2. We send samples to (whoever—whomever) requests them.
3. No one should attempt to iron (her—their) velvet dress.
4. Your protest has been noted. We will give (the same—it) consideration in our new program.
5. (Whoever—Whomever) the company hires will have to be an especially good craftsman.
6. One should clean dirt from garden tools before (they put—he puts) them away.
7. Neither Miss Breen nor (herself—she) thought that the merger would be profitable.
8. I judged the prettiest of the three to be (she—her).
9. The investigating committee, after a thorough inquiry into the case, submitted an exhaustive summary of (their—its) findings.
10. (Do they have—Are there) any fish in the Dead Sea?
11. (A waxed floor's appearance—The appearance of a waxed floor) can be improved by rubbing.
12. (It says in this book—This book says) that the Mayan Indians were fine architects and road builders.
13. Wallace will be greatly pleased over (you—your) recommending him for the position.
14. Each President chooses (their—his) own cabinet.
15. Soup or broth is at (its—their) best when served hot.
16. (Someone else's—Someone's else) tickets were mailed to me by mistake.
17. (Whoever—Whomever) you suggest will receive consideration.
18. Do you think he approves of (me—my) taking a vacation this month?

# Review Test, Verbs, Pronouns, and Possessives

Some of the sentences on this page are incorrect. If a verb, a pronoun, or a possessive is incorrectly used, write the correct form. If a sentence is correct, write C. DO NOT CHANGE ANY SENTENCE THAT IS CORRECT. Do not rewrite the sentence; make the least possible change. Do not change the meaning of the sentence.

1. The men brought us to that new restaurant for dinner last night.
2. No one expected the winner to be him.
3. Either of the men could have lost their balance very easily.
4. Two thirds of his capital are invested in our company.
5. A reward will be paid to whoever returns the purse.
6. Either a blowtorch or an electric reflector heater are useful in thawing frozen water pipes.
7. By taking this bus we will reach the office without having to transfer.
8. One can study best if they can be in a room where the temperature and lighting are correct and where there is no noise.
9. His speech is too long; the audience is leaving one by one.
10. Archimedes proved that a body displaced its own weight in water.
11. The class handed in its papers on the appointed day.
12. You leaving just now will inconvenience us.
13. Each man in the unit had memorized their instructions.
14. The wind's fury slackened and the rain soon ceased.
15. Steve and himself plan to visit South America next year.
16. Soap and water are the safest cleansing agent for this material.
17. It says in the paper that over three hundred million people in the world speak English.
18. I sent you an order four weeks ago, but you have not acknowledged same.
19. They traveled by stagecoach in colonial times.
20. Who does he think could tell us Mr. Foster's new address?
21. Neither the editor nor the publisher were interested in the manuscript.

# Practice Test, Pronouns and Possessives

Some of the sentences on this page are incorrect. If a pronoun or a possessive is incorrectly used, write the correct form. If a sentence is correct, write C. DO NOT CHANGE ANY SENTENCE THAT IS CORRECT. Do not rewrite the sentence; make the least possible change. Do not change the meaning of the sentence.

1. Who shall I say is calling?
2. I cannot return the sample until I receive the same.
3. The book's cover is red and gold.
4. The job will be a challenge to whoever is fortunate enough to get it.
5. When one is tired, you are likely to be less accurate.
6. We show this wall chart to every visitor, whomever he is.
7. Every element in nature has their own atomic weight.
8. He made a mental note of whomever came in late.
9. The cavalry troop led its horses carefully down the steep mountain trail and into the forest.
10. Because of the size of the donation, I believed the donor to be him.
11. My own plans were dependent upon Frank getting the job.
12. Each of the men had his own key to the building.
13. It said in the article that geography is very important in a nation's development.
14. Has anyone exceeded their quota this week?
15. Let whomever has the best sense of direction take the lead.
16. John and myself were both good at drawing.
17. Everyone is required to keep an accurate record of their expenses.
18. When one does their best, it is all they can do.
19. In some Indian villages they make beautiful black pottery.
20. Ellen or Mary would have had the courage to speak for themselves.
21. Both yourself and your partner seem to be busy today.
22. Smith finding the money was only the beginning of our good fortune.

## Adjectives and Adverbs

In each of the following sentences there are two or more words or groups of words in parentheses. Only one of these forms is correct. After number 1 on your strip of paper write the correct form for the first sentence. Do this for the other sentences.

Example: Of the three, Franklin is the (taller—tallest). _____*tallest*

1. Betty is the (best—better) golfer of the foursome.

2. Mr. Perry's explanation of the method was (more—more nearly) complete than mine.

3. There were (fewer—less) children attending school in the United States in 1940 than in 1934.

4. The watchman is older than (any—any other) man on the pay roll.

5. (Fewer—Less) industrial accidents occur when good safety records are rewarded by means of bonuses.

6. I like Ellen's new coat better than her old one. The new one is by far the (prettiest—prettier).

7. Jim's strength is (more—more nearly) equal to the task than Ed's.

8. The Reynolds painting that was on exhibition at the art gallery was more valuable than (any other—any) picture there.

9. The next week there were (less—fewer) absentees than ever.

10. Among all those that I have seen, Carl's stamp collection is (unique—the most unique).

11. Of the two drugstores, Bob thought Grant's the (best—better).

12. Glenn's drawing board appeared to be smoother than (any other—any) I had ever seen.

13. After Paul had machined it, the casting was (squarer—more nearly square) than it had been.

14. (Fewer—Less) people voted in that year than in 1936.

15. Mrs. Hall is the (shrewder—shrewdest) bridge player of the pair.

16. Which one of the trucks is (emptier—more nearly empty)?

## Adjectives and Adverbs

For directions and example, see page 90.

1. These are the shoes (and—and the) stockings I wore in the pageant.
2. He wanted to (bluntly ask—ask bluntly) why the deficit had not been discovered earlier.
3. Jane was (very—very much) pleased when her suggestion was adopted.
4. We (nearly spent—spent nearly) a thousand dollars on advertising.
5. As soon as she had spoken, Louise regretted the hasty (and—and the) ill-considered answer.
6. The Carters have bought a house (and—and a) lot at 76 Lane Street.
7. They asked me to (quickly estimate—estimate quickly) the cost of redecorating.
8. The captain was (too—too much) disturbed by the umpire's decision to concentrate on the next play.
9. The white-haired man had a tanned (and—and a) weather-beaten face that indicated an outdoor life.
10. The discovery of the wheel (and the—and) axle was a milestone of progress.
11. Bob (came only—only came) to return the book he had borrowed.
12. I was (too—too greatly) startled by the apparition to scream.
13. When she fell, she (nearly broke—broke nearly) every dish on the tray.
14. Tell him to (carefully read—read carefully) any paper he signs.
15. I can (only endure this—endure this only) a few minutes.
16. Two men sat with a black (and—and a) red checkerboard between them.
17. The listeners were (very—very much) impressed by his earnestness.
18. He wanted us to (think first—first think) and answer later.
19. The bread (and—and the) butter seemed more delicious than anything he had ever eaten before.
20. I (almost saw—saw almost) all the steps in the making of rayon.

# Review Test, Verbs, Pronouns, Possessives, Adjectives, and Adverbs

Some of the sentences on this page are incorrect. If a verb, a pronoun, a possessive, an adjective, or an adverb is incorrectly used, write the correct form. If a sentence is correct, write C. DO NOT CHANGE ANY SENTENCE THAT IS CORRECT. Do not rewrite the sentence; make the least possible change. Do not change the meaning of the sentence.

1. Ray would have liked to have been a doctor.

2. Water is more plentiful than any liquid.

3. Whoever you expected to telephone you has not done so.

4. Either a window pole or a stepladder is needed to close the window.

5. There were less automobile accidents this year than last year.

6. When the group dispersed, it went off in twos and threes.

7. The long and the rambling speech was printed in the record.

8. The road was too curved to permit fast driving.

9. I did not realize that whooping cough was contagious.

10. Give the message to whomever comes in first.

11. The larder was more empty than usual.

12. The old warehouse stood at the street's end.

13. I hope you don't believe the writer of that letter to be I.

14. Everyone who keeps house has their own favorite recipes.

15. Neither the knife nor the nails are rustproof.

16. His sister can almost read any shorthand.

17. My father and myself are in business together.

18. Since she has been taking this treatment, she has had fewer colds.

19. "Never again will they quote me without permission!" he raged.

20. Arthur is the tallest of the three, but John weighs the most.

21. It shows in the picture how to set up the apparatus.

22. The hour and minute when the train arrives are printed on the schedule.

23. He neglected to thoroughly clean the carburetor.

24. Gerald often went to New York, but his partner never had until last week.

# Prepositions

In each of the following sentences there are two or more words or groups of words in parentheses. Only one of these forms is correct. After number 1 on your strip of paper write the correct form for the first sentence. Do this for the other sentences.

Example: I was the last to (finish—finish up). _____*finish*

1. The travelers (divided—divided up) their provisions.
2. The firm's reputation would suffer if it strained its credit (in that—that) way.
3. Columbus sighted land (October 12—on October 12).
4. My advice (was—was of) no use; Grant sold the stock anyway.
5. Don't (start in—start) to cut your material until you have laid out your entire pattern.
6. With the tubes burned out, the radio (was—was of) no use to Matt.
7. He cannot be promoted if he continues to neglect his work (in this—this) way.
8. Florida was discovered (on Easter Sunday—Easter Sunday).
9. Her ability to speak Spanish (was—was of) little use to her in Brazil.
10. The committee heard and considered the arguments of both sides, and (that—in that) way the question was decided fairly.
11. The freight was sent to you (on March 12—March 12).
12. He stood there with his chest (expanded—expanded out).
13. The picture was hung (in back of—behind) a convenient door.
14. If you examine the basis for your prejudices (that—in that) way, they will probably disappear.
15. Is the FBI (investigating—investigating into) the case?
16. A man standing (in back of—behind) the wire caught the foul.
17. It will be (no use—of no use) to plant peas so late in the season.
18. Don't walk too (near—near to) the edge of the cliff.

# Prepositions

For directions and example, see page 93.

1. He poured a gallon of syrup (into—in) the container.
2. Daylight-saving time is different (than—from) sun time.
3. Dorothy's actions made me angry (with—at) her for a minute.
4. The two rows of grinding machinery were placed so that there was plenty of walking space (among—between) them.
5. The attorney was ushered (in—into) the vice president's office.
6. I did become angry (with—at) the overcharge, but I was not angry (at—with) the saleswoman.
7. The reward was distributed (between—among) the five men who had captured the thief.
8. His version of the incident was different (than—from) yours.
9. Mark became angry (at—with) the suggestion that he had been careless.
10. The horses were herded (in—into) the corral.
11. All the neighbors decided (among—between) themselves what to send.
12. Madge sings that song differently (than—from) you.
13. Don't be angry (with—at) me; I didn't mean to do it.
14. There was great rivalry (among—between) the teams, since both were striving for the state championship.
15. Sutton talked differently (than—from) Coleman.
16. Blake was angry (with—at) the boys who broke his window.
17. Each one of us dropped a coin (in—into) the beggar's cup.
18. The plane fell (among—between) two trees, shearing off both wings.
19. The procedure was different (from—than) the one he had planned.
20. There was dissension (among—between) the members of the crew.
21. He was angry (with—at) the selfishness of their actions.
22. On our Washington tour we went (in—into) the Library of Congress.
23. Our company's advertising methods are different (than—from) theirs.

# Review Test, Verbs, Pronouns, Possessives, Adjectives, Adverbs, and Prepositions

Some of the sentences on this page are incorrect. If a verb, a pronoun, a possessive, an adjective, an adverb, or a preposition is incorrectly used, write the correct form. If a sentence is correct, write C. DO NOT CHANGE ANY SENTENCE THAT IS CORRECT. Do not rewrite the sentence; make the least possible change. Do not change the meaning of the sentence.

1. When Burns or Brown run for office, I remind all my friends to vote.
2. The engraving was the most perfect he had produced.
3. Who do you suppose wrote this unsigned letter?
4. We expect to meet your field manager in New York Saturday.
5. The plumber and himself agreed that a force cup would open the stopped drain.
6. Of all the cars we have seen this one seems the better buy.
7. We played chess while the rest of the party was dancing.
8. The firm maintained a frequent and a prompt delivery service.
9. His books were little use to him after his eyesight had failed.
10. The tire was too worn to be used with safety.
11. Everybody in these offices is responsible for his own mail.
12. The Iroquois Indians lived differently than the Navahos.
13. There is no use in knocking; they are not at home.
14. The cup and the saucer slipped from his hands and broke.
15. The flowers in our garden are all withered up.
16. They call the speaker's stand the rostrum.
17. Surplus earnings were shared between all the stockholders.
18. Professor Woods was angry at the habitual latecomers.
19. If the stain had been removed, I could have worn the coat yesterday.
20. The ball was just in back of the ten-yard line when the half ended.
21. Re-read the letter before you put it in the envelope.
22. Dr. Eff can almost recognize any dialect.
23. There are less mistakes in your typing since your speed has increased.

# Conjunctions

In each of the following sentences there are two or more words or groups of words in parentheses. Only one of these forms is correct. After number 1 on your strip of paper write the correct form for the first sentence. Do this for the other sentences.

1. Mr. Lamb did not know (if—whether) he should renew the lease or not.

2. The new studio is as bright (if not brighter than the old—as the old, if not brighter).

3. The patch was cut one-half inch wider than the hole (so—so that) it would hold securely.

4. Rob thought the cure as bad (as the cold, if not worse—if not worse than the cold).

5. Nobody could tell (if—whether) the ropes would hold or not.

6. A tunnel had been drilled through the mountain (so—so that) the trains could run through.

7. Trent asked (if—whether) the packages had arrived.

8. The mixture was as thick (if not thicker than molasses—as molasses, if not thicker).

9. We phoned the sheriff (so that—so) we might verify the story.

10. He doubted (if—whether) a laboratory analysis would give a clue.

11. He said he had paid as much (as it was worth, if not more—if not more than it was worth).

12. He oiled his hands thoroughly with linseed oil (so—so that) he could remove the paint from them.

13. Louis was not sure (if—whether) Mr. Green would agree or not.

14. He delayed as long (if not longer than was wise—as was wise, if not longer).

15. I had to decide (if—whether) I wanted the book or not.

16. The mechanic used a lock washer (so that—so) the bolt would not work loose and fall off.

# Reference Section Drill, Adjectives, Adverbs, Prepositions, and Conjunctions

Write the headings *Rule* and *Correct Form* on your strip of paper.

For each sentence refer to your reference section, find the rule that explains the correct usage, and write the number of the rule under the heading *Rule*. Then write the correct form under the heading *Correct Form*.

For this page refer to rules 119—120; 122—123; 125a; 127a; 137—139; 148—154; 157; 159; 172; 174—175.

1. Stains can be more safely removed from a waffle iron with soda than with (any—any other) cleansing agent.
2. Morrison seems (very—very much) refreshed after his vacation.
3. (On Monday—Monday) evening the bowling team meets.
4. Gasoline rationing resulted in (fewer—less) cars on the road.
5. If you (divide—divide up) the work improperly, confusion may result.
6. Bob's luck was good; he (won nearly—nearly won) every game he played.
7. Among the council members, Jackson had the (better—best) mind.
8. Take these books; they are (no use—of no use) to me.
9. The chief's car was painted a brilliant (and—and a) fiery red.
10. It was apparent that the customer was angry (with—at) the waitress.
11. This window screen is (more—more nearly) square than that one.
12. No one knew (if—whether) the ship could be floated or not.
13. He seemed puzzled over the motive (behind—in back of) my remark.
14. Just as I went (in—into) the store, I saw you across the street.
15. The carpenter used a brace (and—and a) bit to bore the hole.
16. The book said to (next nail the lid on—nail the lid on next).
17. He read as long (if not longer than the light was good—as the light was good, if not longer).
18. Never before have I known Smith to act (that way—in that way).
19. There is a traditional rivalry (between—among) the four schools.
20. Tom wished he were older (so—so that) he might join the Navy.
21. This dog was marked differently (than—from) the rest of the litter.

# Review Test, Verbs, Pronouns, Possessives, Adjectives, Adverbs, Prepositions, and Conjunctions

Some of the sentences on this page are incorrect. If a word is incorrectly used, write the correct form. If a sentence is correct, write C. DO NOT CHANGE ANY SENTENCE THAT IS CORRECT. Do not rewrite the sentences; make the least possible change. Do not change the meaning of the sentence.

1. Neither of the elevators were working, so we walked up the stairs.
2. For his lunch, Wilson started in with fruit juice.
3. Of my two visitors, Mark came most frequently, but Alfred stayed longest.
4. A check or a money order were usually required.
5. Bud swims as well if not better than his brother.
6. Whom did he say operated the switchboard last night?
7. Our car was in back of a huge truck most of the way.
8. May I ask if the manager is here tonight?
9. Tom was too stunned by his fall to cry for help.
10. The bad news have already made him change his plans.
11. It has already snowed as much if not more than it snowed last winter.
12. Handmade Irish lace is prettier than any lace.
13. Whoever you see in the inspection room, report to me.
14. I learned that water expanded when it froze.
15. He sent the letter by air mail so it would reach us on time.
16. Let us divide the work equally among the two of us.
17. When you have finished the letter, drop it into the nearest mail box.
18. A number of points on the projector require frequent oiling.
19. Paul took the wheel so I could rest.
20. This way, each applicant will be notified without waiting.
21. They use llamas instead of horses in the Andes.
22. Tell me if you think I should return the hat or not.
23. As we waited, it never seemed that you would come.

# Practice Test, Adjectives, Adverbs, Prepositions, and Conjunctions

Some of the sentences on this page are incorrect. If an adjective, an adverb, a preposition, or a conjunction is incorrectly used, write the correct form. If a sentence is correct, write C. DO NOT CHANGE ANY SENTENCE THAT IS CORRECT. Do not rewrite the sentence; make the least possible change. Do not change the meaning of the sentence.

1. It was a warm and a hospitable room if ever I saw one.
2. Texas is larger than any state in the Union.
3. Even a short nap seems to make him feel rested up.
4. It was agreed between the three experts that the plan was faulty.
5. In back of this thriving industry was the genius of one man.
6. It was hard to guess which one of the twins weighed the most.
7. To completely refuse the request was more than I could do.
8. How can you tell if the bank statement is correct or not?
9. Will the cleaner return my blue dress Saturday?
10. There is rivalry between the many manufacturers in this field.
11. His self-confidence was quite different than my clumsy efforts.
12. The new light-weight alloy is as strong if not stronger than the finest steel formerly used.
13. This table is similar in design to the other, but the top is rounder.
14. He started in at ten o'clock and was all finished up at five.
15. The office boy led him in a small cubbyhole of an office.
16. The finish of this piece is different from a varnished finish.
17. Mr. Brown seemed very moved by the loyalty of his employees.
18. Your contributing this way is something we had not anticipated.
19. John has only worked here one month.
20. She rose at six so she would not delay the others.
21. Walters was angry at the salesgirl who had kept him waiting.
22. Less than ten drivers attempted to travel on the icy road.
23. That book will be no use to you in this course.

# Punctuation and Sentence Structure

Some of the groups of words on this page contain errors in sentence structure. Write the correct form on your strip of paper as indicated in the sample. If a sentence is correct, write C. DO NOT CHANGE ANY SENTENCE THAT IS CORRECT.

Example: Where did you put the pan, that needs soldering? ___*pan that*

1. For this job we need men, who understand radio and elementary physics.
2. John who understood radio and elementary physics asked the lecturer a shrewd question about one point he had made.
3. This model has been bought by a manufacturer which won the prize.
4. I was permitted to examine Mr. Grover's bookplates, who is a collector, you know.
5. The book that she was reading yesterday tells of the heroic life of Jadwiga, a Polish princess.
6. The sketch was adapted from one of Bewick's etchings, who was a famous engraver.
7. Mrs. Carver's new coat which is of good material and well tailored was bought at Miller's.
8. We brought along some of Bing Crosby's records, who is Jack's favorite singer.
9. The custom was to recommend for advancement the five men, whose production had been highest for the month.
10. Since he was in a hurry, he took a plane rather than a train which would get him to Chicago faster.
11. Ruth's hair which was golden and curly was her most attractive feature.
12. Mr. Leach, who is a tax specialist, disagrees with that theory.
13. This is the coat, that I saw described in the advertisement in yesterday's paper.
14. I admire the announcer's enunciation who handles the morning radio programs.

## Punctuation and Sentence Structure

For directions and example, see page 100.

1. Due to bad weather, the game was postponed until the next day.

2. Ray lost his watch, which his father had given him, and had belonged originally to a soldier hero at Bataan.

3. If the stencil is sharply cut, the copies should be satisfactory if the typing is accurate.

4. Jim realized to drive over the ice-covered roads was extremely dangerous.

5. You should open the mail when I am not here and I am busy with something else.

6. I am enclosing Martin's time card, who asked me to send it to you.

7. After he had sealed the envelope, George remembered the check, after he had stamped the envelope.

8. Dorothy feels to accept another's hospitality and then to criticize him is a mark of bad breeding.

9. I was disappointed when he did not answer my first letter and he telegraphed that he could not come home.

10. The train crash was due to one engineer's having run past a signal.

11. I have lost a wrench, that belongs to the foreman.

12. Jerry advanced rapidly in his profession, due to his ability to handle men.

13. Mrs. Black thought to clean enameled furniture a solution of bicarbonate of soda should be used.

14. Because it was raining, Sue wore her raincoat to the office because she didn't want to carry an umbrella.

15. Mr. Gray's desk calendar which had been lost for a week turned up in place mysteriously one morning.

16. Lowell recovered from his illness due to good nursing and care.

# Review Test, Verbs, Pronouns, Possessives, Adjectives, Adverbs, Conjunctions, Punctuation, and Sentence Structure

Some of the sentences on this page contain errors. If a sentence is correct, write C. If a sentence is incorrect, make the least possible change that will correct it. Do not change the meaning of any sentence.

1. Bring these magazines with you when you go; I have read all of them.
2. Will anyone who has finished bring their papers to me?
3. According to the newspapers, the factory will open Friday.
4. She speaks French as well if not better than a native.
5. Pike's Peak is better known than any mountain in the United States.
6. Pauline and myself took our vacations together.
7. There were less doctors in the town than the population called for.
8. This is Anna Darvin, who will assist you in the art department.
9. The new shipping instructions are different than those we have been following.
10. We performed an experiment to show that water was composed of oxygen and hydrogen.
11. The forecast doesn't say if we shall have snow on Wednesday or not.
12. After resting up for a week, the men were ready to go back to work.
13. Do you know whom is coming with the Cranes tonight?
14. Be sure to tell Mrs. Martin when you will arrive and you expect to leave.
15. Our neighbors only moved here last January.
16. I want the records for Mr. Weber who will examine them.
17. The opinions of the audience differed, as its responses showed.
18. Mr. Carey was too amused at their tale to be very angry with them.
19. When you come in, don't look surprised when you see Albert.
20. Due to his interest in medicine, he was assigned to the hospital corps.
21. My predicament would have amused whoever had a sense of humor.
22. The desk came from my aunt's childhood home, who willed it to me.
23. Mr. Johnson is angry with the lack of attention to his complaint

# Practice Test, Punctuation and Sentence Structure

For directions and example, see page 100.

1. Where is the map, that you mentioned in your letter?

2. He gave a talk after the dinner which was interesting and appropriate.

3. Mary has done well on the radio due to her dramatic training.

4. Carl's book which was a biography of Woodrow Wilson lay open on the table.

5. I received Glenn's note, whom I had expected to meet later.

6. We saw the places where Washington was born and he is buried.

7. Due to a breakdown in the machinery, we did not work this morning.

8. Tennis is the only game, that Jim has learned to play well.

9. The lawyer found a clause in the contract that released Mr. Peters from liability.

10. Father thinks to repair a garden hose with friction tape is only a temporary measure.

11. For the leading role they chose Caroline Hardy who sings well.

12. My sister Rita, who joined the Women's Army Corps, was sent to North Africa.

13. If you would take some aspirin, you might get rid of your headache, if you would lie down.

14. Hannah knew to use gasoline for cleaning clothing involves considerable danger.

15. Mr. Roberts who knows me well will cash the check for you.

16. While I sat in the hall, Mrs. Archer came in while I waited for Mr. Hubbard.

17. The dealer warned us to make the repairs ourselves would require a great amount of time and patience.

18. I have been using Miss Bronson's files, who has a complete record of the case.

# Comprehensive Test, Parts One, Two, and Three

Some of the following sentences are incorrect. Write the correction on your strip of paper on lines numbered to correspond to those in the test. If a sentence is correct, write C. DO NOT CHANGE ANY SENTENCE THAT IS CORRECT. Do not rewrite any sentence; make the least possible change. Do not change the meaning of any sentence.

In this test consider verbs, pronouns, possessives, adjectives, adverbs, prepositions, capitalization, punctuation, and sentence structure.

## Part One

1. I had laid down to rest and had fallen asleep.
2. Jim and Louise expect to buy a new house soon.
3. He pretended good enough to deceive me.
4. The golden voice sent it's tones throughout the theater.
5. You should have heard how beautiful she played!
6. I could of done better if I had had more time.
7. Tell the other men and us where to begin working.
8. Howard belongs to a greek-letter fraternity.
9. Hadn't we ought to increase our sales force next month?
10. Will you tell me Grant how long you will be away?
11. This typewriter is all right, I put a new ribbon on it.
12. An Admiral will be the guest of honor tonight.
13. The bell sounds loudly when everything else is still.
14. He expects to be transferred to Springfield Ohio next week.
15. All our seamen's names are on the honor list.
16. Mary says that everyone except she has received a raise.
17. She asked whether it is true "that a barking dog never bites."
18. No workers could have excelled Brad and him.
19. Eddie was disappointed to find that the west isn't wild.
20. You told us to find a set of blocks and we looked in every store and then we bought some but the baby didn't like them and she wouldn't play with them.

*(Continue with item 21 on page 105.)*

## Part Two

21. Neither article mention the real cause of the accident.

22. That was a real charitable thing to say.

23. There was no one else like him.

24. I remember of writing an order for those supplies.

25. That sure was a fast ocean liner.

26. Your latest request, as well as earlier ones, are being attended to today.

27. It couldn't have been she who left the package.

28. The governor and lieutenant governor will attend the dinner.

29. The purpose of visiting that country, is to study the habits of the people.

30. Jim is one of those persons who has to be reminded.

31. Verdi was a more renowned composer than a conductor.

32. The story tells of a man whom we know really lived.

33. After they became partners Meyer and Jones built a new plant.

34. If he would phone this evening, say that we have gone out.

35. The reason for his silence was because he knew no English.

36. Michelangelo was a famous painter and a sculptor.

37. Post's and Gatty's record-making flight was made in 1931.

38. I shall speak plainly so that all might understand.

39. Did Fred say we can use his encyclopedia?

40. Fewer people die with appendicitis now than formerly.

41. Will I use wax crayon or pastel for the portrait?

42. Each swimmer will be given the following, a suit, a towel, and a bathing cap.

43. His election I might remark would be a serious mistake.

44. The critics differ from one another about this play.

45. A quitclaim deed is when the seller merely releases whatever claim he may have to the property he is selling.

46. The reason for its being chosen is, that the book is really good.

(*Continue with item 47 on page 106.*)

47. In his younger days he wrote fiction, poetry, biographies, and published books.
48. The files were well kept, and we could not find the correspondence.
49. Listening carefully, the crickets' chirps come faster.
50. He spoke like we thought he would speak.
51. Unless neatly mended, you should not wear the coat again.
52. Marcia stopped to talk with us and her new hat looked lovely.
53. "Ned, why didn't you say, "Excuse me," and leave?" asked Tom.
54. Jim knew welding, riveting, and how to read blueprints.

## Part Three

55. Between Dickens and Thackeray, I like the former best.
56. Whom did you say wanted to speak to the foreman?
57. Neither Polly nor Ann have made any sacrifice.
58. Couldn't you divide up the work more fairly?
59. Whoever I find sleeping in class will be dismissed at once.
60. Helen dresses as well if not better than Joan.
61. Marvin gave me my choice among the many valuable souvenirs.
62. Assign this machine to whomever you think is capable of operating it.
63. The class expressed its different opinions one by one.
64. The new clerk who is also a rapid typist seems very pleasant.
65. We received a letter from a new customer which contained a money order.
66. My assistant has less file cases than I have.
67. I walked in the coffee shop and sat down.
68. The map showed that the Pacific was extremely wide.
69. Let anyone, who types rapidly, report for work tomorrow.
70. We knew the author to be him.
71. One of the packages was delivered Saturday.
72. He will leave that room only over my dead body!
73. Everyone knew their own locker number.
74. Terry said that his brother and himself were printers.
75. His greatest pride was his son's career, who was an opera singer.

# Allocation of Reference Section Rules by Parts

## Part One

*Verbs*

| | | | | | |
|---|---|---|---|---|---|
| 21 | 21e | 26 | 29 | 37 | 40a |
| 21a | 21f | 26a | 29a | 38 | 58 |
| 21b | 22 | 27 | 30 | 38a | 59 |
| 21c | 23 | 27a | 30a | 39 | 60 |
| 21d | 23a | 28 | 36 | 40 | 61 |

*Nouns, Pronouns, and Possessives*

| | | | | | |
|---|---|---|---|---|---|
| 77 | 79 | 81a | 82b | 100 | 100b |
| 77a | 80 | 82 | 95 | 100a | 102 |
| 78 | 81 | 82a | 96 | | |

*Adjectives and Adverbs*

| | | | | | |
|---|---|---|---|---|---|
| 110 | 116a | 117a | 124 | 131 | 133 |
| 111 | 117 | 118 | 130 | 132 | 136 |
| 116 | | | | | |

*Prepositions*

| | | | |
|---|---|---|---|
| 141 | 144 | 146 | **147** |

*Capitalization*

| | | | | | |
|---|---|---|---|---|---|
| 177 | 180 | 183 | 186 | 189a | 192 |
| 178 | 181 | 184 | 187 | 189b | 193 |
| 178a | 181a | 184a | 188 | 190 | 194 |
| 179 | 182 | 185 | 189 | 191 | |

*Punctuation*

| | | | | | |
|---|---|---|---|---|---|
| 195 | 197 | 200 | 210 | 214 | 218 |
| 196 | 198 | 206 | 211 | 215 | 219 |
| 196a | 198a | 207 | 212 | 216 | 220 |

*Sentence Structure*

| | | | |
|---|---|---|---|
| 228 | 229 | 231 | **233** |

## Part Two

*Verbs*

| | | | | | |
|---|---|---|---|---|---|
| 24 | 32 | 42 | 50 | 55 | 57 |
| 25 | 33 | 42a | 51 | 56 | 62b |
| 31 | 40b | 45 | 54 | 56a | 64 |

*Nouns, Pronouns, and Possessives*

| | | | | | |
|---|---|---|---|---|---|
| 77b | 83 | 84b | 93a | 101 | 101b |
| 81b | 84a | 93 | 94 | 101a | |

*Adjectives and Adverbs*

| | | | | | |
|---|---|---|---|---|---|
| 112 | 115 | 126 | 128 | 129 | 134 |
| 113 | 121 | 127 | 128a | 133a | 135 |
| 114 | 125 | | | | |

*Prepositions*

| | | | | | |
|---|---|---|---|---|---|
| 140 | 142 | 143 | 145 | 155 | 156 |

*Prepositions* (continued)

| | | | |
|---|---|---|---|
| 158 | 160 | 161 | 162 |

*Conjunctions*

| | | | | | |
|---|---|---|---|---|---|
| 164b | 166 | 168 | 170 | 171a | 173a |
| 165 | 167 | 169 | **171** | 173 | 176 |

*Punctuation*

| | | | | |
|---|---|---|---|---|
| 199 | 203 | 205 | 209 | 217 |
| 201 | 204 | 208 | 213 | 221 |

*Sentence Structure*

| | | | | | |
|---|---|---|---|---|---|
| 230 | 235 | 239 | 243 | 245 | 247 |
| 232 | 236 | 241 | 244 | 246 | 249 |
| 234 | 238 | | | | |

## Part Three

*Verbs*

| | | | | | |
|---|---|---|---|---|---|
| 34 | 41a | 46 | 49 | 62 | 63 |
| 35 | 43 | 47 | 52 | 62a | 65 |
| 41 | 44 | 48 | 53 | 62c | 66 |

*Nouns, Pronouns, and Possessives*

| | | | | | |
|---|---|---|---|---|---|
| 84c | 86 | 90 | 96a | 99 | 103 |
| 84d | 88 | 91 | 97 | 102a | 104 |
| 85 | 89 | 92 | 98 | | |

*Adjectives and Adverbs*

| | | | | | |
|---|---|---|---|---|---|
| 119 | 122 | 125a | 137 | 138 | 139 |
| 120 | 123 | 127a | | | |

*Prepositions*

| | | | | | |
|---|---|---|---|---|---|
| 148 | 150 | 152 | **154** | **157** | 159 |
| 149 | 151 | 153 | | | |

*Conjunctions*

| | |
|---|---|
| 172 | 174 | 175 |

*Punctuation and Sentence Structure*

| | | | | | |
|---|---|---|---|---|---|
| 202 | 226a | 237 | 240 | 242 | 248 |
| 226 | 233a | 238a | | | |

# REFERENCE SECTION
## SENTENCES AND PARTS OF SPEECH

In nearly all our speaking and writing, we arrange our words into groups that express complete thoughts. Each group of words names an object or person or idea and tells or asks something about the person or thing named. Such a group of words is a *sentence*.

**1. A sentence has two parts. The part that names the person or thing told or asked about is the *subject*. The part that tells or asks something about the subject is the *predicate*. If one of these parts is omitted, the group of words is not a sentence.**

In the following sentences the subject is printed in italics.
Example 1.   *Tropical fish* often are brightly colored.
Example 2.   When did *John and his brother* come?
Example 3.   *The man in the gray suit* asked us what we wanted.
In sentences 4 and 5 the predicate is printed in italics.
Example 4.   Every member of the club *voted*.
Example 5.   We *looked at all the books and selected several that related to American history*.

**2. A sentence must express a complete thought. A group of words that does not do this should not be written as though it were a sentence.**

In example 5 above, the group of words *that related to American history* has a subject, *that,* and a predicate, *related to American history*. This group of words is not a sentence, however, because it does not express a complete thought. It is a *subordinate clause*. The rest of example 5 is the *principal clause* or *main clause* of the sentence.

**3. A sentence that makes a statement is a *declarative* sentence. A sentence that asks a question is an *interrogative* sentence. A sentence that gives a command or makes a request is an *imperative* sentence.**

*Note:* The subject of an imperative sentence is *you,* that is, the person to whom the request or command is addressed. This *you* is rarely actually spoken or written, but is understood. Thus we say that *you,* understood, is the subject of a sentence like *Take off your coat.*

108

**4. Every sentence begins with a capital letter. Every declarative or imperative sentence ends with a period, unless it is an exclamation, which requires an exclamation point. Every interrogative sentence ends with a question mark.**

Example 1. We came to a very rough road. (declarative)
Example 2. Drive slowly over this rough road. (imperative)
Example 3. What a rough road this is! (exclamation)
Example 4. What is the name of this road? (interrogative)

Each word in a sentence has a particular function to perform. Words are classified according to the functions they perform.

**5. A word that names a person, place, thing, condition, or quality is called a *noun*. Some nouns are *Paul, Omaha, table, loneliness, happiness*.**

**6. In order to avoid awkward repetition of nouns, we frequently use words that stand for nouns. A word used in place of a noun is called a *pronoun*. Among the pronouns are *he, you, we, us, her, who*, and *which*.**

**7. A word that expresses action or being is a *verb*. In the following sentences the words in italics are verbs: Tom *threw* the ball. Your hat *is* on the table. The house *seems* deserted.**

*Note:* Every sentence must have a noun or pronoun to name the person or thing told about and a verb to tell something about that person or thing. The following is a sentence: *Men work.* Here *men* is the subject and *work* is the predicate. Most of our sentences are longer, such as *The men who are building the new bridge work very hard.* In this sentence *men* is the essential word in the subject, or the *simple subject,* and *work* is the essential word in the predicate, or the *simple predicate* (sometimes called the *predicate verb*).

Some words change or limit or add to the meaning of other words. We say that they *modify* other words.

**8. A word that modifies a noun is called an *adjective*. An adjective may tell the size, shape, color, or quality, or it may point out, or tell the number. The following are examples of adjectives: *small, round, blue, comfortable, those, seven*.**

**9. A word that is used to modify a verb or an adjective is called an *adverb*. An adverb may also modify another adverb. Adverbs answer the questions *How?*, *When?*, *Where?*, and *To what extent?* The following are adverbs: *quickly, then, everywhere, fully*.**

**10.** Words like *by, over, in, for,* and *to* are called *prepositions.* A preposition is followed by a noun or pronoun, called its *object,* and shows the relation between its object and some other word in the sentence. The preposition with its object forms a *prepositional phrase.* The following are examples of prepositional phrases: *on the porch, for him, with Mary.*

10a. A prepositional phrase may be used as an adjective or as an adverb.

Example 1.   The girl *with the red hat* is Helen.
Example 2.   Mr. Stanton lives *in Baltimore.*

In example 1, *with the red hat* is an adjective phrase modifying the noun *girl.* In example 2, *in Baltimore* is an adverbial phrase modifying the verb *lives.*

**11.  In addition to single words and phrases, subordinate clauses may be used as modifiers.**

Example 1.   The man *who is sitting in the outer office* wants to see Mr. Jones.
Example 2.   *When the whistle blew,* Frank ran to his post.

In example 1, *who is sitting in the outer office* is an adjective clause modifying the noun *man.* In example 2, *when the whistle blew* is an adverbial clause modifying the verb *ran.*

**12.  A word used to join words, phrases, or clauses is a *conjunction.*  Some conjunctions are *and, but, or, when, that,* and *if.* Subordinate clauses often begin with conjunctions.**

**13.  A word used to express some emotion and having no grammatical connection with a sentence is called an *interjection.* Some interjections are *Alas!, Aha!, Oh!, Hurrah!***

**14.  The part of speech that a word is depends upon how it is used in a sentence.  The same word may be several different parts of speech in different sentences.**

Example 1.   That *light* hurts my eyes.
Example 2.   Jane is wearing a *light* coat.
Example 3.   The boys always *light* the fire for us.

In example 1, the word *light* is a noun, in example 2 it is an adjective, and in example 3 it is a verb.

## VERBS

**15.** Very often a verb expresses action that is done to some person or some thing, and the sense is not complete until we know who or what is the receiver of the action. The words *Robert threw* do not ordinarily convey a complete idea, because we do not know what or whom he threw. When we say *Robert threw the ball,* the sense is complete because the receiver of the action, the *ball,* is named. **A verb that requires a receiver of the action expressed by it is a *transitive* verb.**

**15a.** Some verbs express action that is complete without a receiver. For example, *Robert laughed* is a complete idea. A verb that does not require a receiver of the action it expresses is an *intransitive* verb.

**15b.** Some verbs may be transitive or intransitive, depending upon how they are used.

Example 1. Alice *sang* very well at the concert.
Example 2. Alice *sang* a new song last night.
In example 1 *sang* is intransitive; in example 2 it is transitive.

**16. Certain intransitive verbs which do not express real action are called *linking verbs* or *copulas*. The verbs in italics in the following sentences are linking verbs.**

Example 1. Mr. Brown *is* treasurer of the company.
Example 2. The children *seem* happy in their new school.

**17. When the subject of a verb names the person or thing that *performs* the action, the verb is said to be in the *active voice*. In the two sentences that follow, the verbs are in the active voice.**

Example 1. Ted *ran* swiftly down the stairs.
Example 2. Miss Clark *opened* the box.

**17a.** The word that names the receiver of the action of a transitive verb in the active voice is called the *object* of the verb.

In example 2 the verb, *opened,* is transitive. The word *box* names the receiver of the action. *Box* is therefore the object of the verb *opened* in example 2.

**17b.** When the subject of a verb names the person or thing that *receives* the action, the verb is in the *passive voice*. In the sentences that follow, the verbs are in the passive voice.

Example 1. Sam and his brother *have been invited.*
The subject, *Sam and his brother,* receives the action of the verb *have been invited.* The performer of the action is not named.
Example 2. The box *was opened* by Miss Clark.

The subject *box* receives the action of the verb *was opened.* Here the performer of the action is named in a prepositional phrase, *by Miss Clark,* modifying the verb.

18. Verbs have different forms to indicate the person spoken about (*person*), whether one person is spoken about or more than one (*number*), and the time of the action expressed (*tense*). **When the subject of the verb is the person who is speaking, the verb is in the** *first person* **(I go, I am going). When the subject of the verb is the person spoken to, the verb is in the** *second person* **(you go, you have gone). When the subject of the verb is someone other than the speaker or the person spoken to, the verb is in the** *third person* **(he goes, they have gone).**

18a. If the subject of the verb is one person or thing, the verb is *singular* in *number.* If the subject is more than one person or thing, the verb is *plural* in *number.*

|  | *Singular* | *Plural* |
|---|---|---|
| **First Person** | I do | We do |
| **Second Person** | You do | You do |
| **Third Person** | John does | The girls do |

With the exception of the verb *to be,* which has the form *am* for the first person singular, the only change made in a verb form to express person and number is in the third person singular. The third person singular, present tense, is regularly formed by adding *s* (or sometimes *es*) to the form used for the other persons, for example: I *walk,* you *walk,* they *walk,* but he *walks.* Exceptions to this rule are the third person singular forms *has* and *is.*

18b. Typical variations in verb forms to express different times at which the action of the verb takes place are as follows:

*Present Tense:* They *walk* five miles every day. (This is a statement of present fact.)

*Present Progressive:* I *am walking* as fast as possible. (This expresses a continuing action taking place in the present time.)

*Past:* Bob *walked* to town yesterday. (The action took place in the past.)

*Future:* They *will walk* from the park to the river. (The action is to take place in the future.)

*Present Perfect:* Mr. Brown *has walked* all the way from Riverdale. (The action at the present time has been completed.)

*Past Perfect:* We *had walked* half a mile when we met Mary and Bill. (The action was completed at some past time, before something else took place.)

**19. Each verb has four main forms, from some of which the other tenses are formed. These are the *principal parts* of the verb.** Their names, and the principal parts of four verbs, are as follows:

| *Present* | *Past* | *Present Participle* | *Past Participle* |
|-----------|--------|----------------------|-------------------|
| collect | collected | collecting | collected |
| invite | invited | inviting | invited |
| see | saw | seeing | seen |
| hold | held | holding | held |

**In many verbs the past tense and the past participle are the same, and are formed by adding *ed* or *d* to the present. Many of the most frequently used verbs, however, have different forms for the past tense and the past participle.**

**19a.** Verbs have two forms in which they perform some of the functions of nouns. These are the *infinitive* and the *gerund*.

The infinitive consists of the present tense of the verb preceded by *to*: *to go, to walk.*

Example 1.  *To retreat* is impossible.
The infinitive *to retreat* is the subject of this sentence.

Sometimes the *to* is omitted in using the infinitive.

Example 2.  Can't you make him *hear?*
In this sentence the word *hear* is an infinitive.

The gerund is the same in form as the present participle: *going, walking.*

Example 3.  *Swimming* tires me very quickly.
In this sentence the gerund *swimming* is the subject.

**20. Verbs that are used with the principal parts of other verbs to form various tenses, or to express the passive voice, are called *auxiliary verbs* or *auxiliaries*.**

In the following examples the auxiliaries are in italics.

He *is* going.                    The vase *had been* broken.
I *shall* see you.                They *would* not go.
Jim *has* come in.                The letters *were* written.

A verb with its auxiliaries is called a *verb phrase.* For example, *is going, has come, would go,* and *had been broken* are verb phrases.

# I. Correct Use of Tenses

**21. Never use the past participle (19) of a verb for the simple past tense. Never join auxiliary verb forms, such as *has*, *have*, *had*, *was*, and *were*, to the simple past tense. Use these words with the past participle to form perfect tenses and the passive voice.**

**21a.** The past tenses of the verbs *come, run, begin, drink, ring,* and *sing* are as follows: *came, ran, began, drank, rang,* and *sang.* Do not use auxiliary verbs with these past tenses. The past participles are *come, run, begun, drunk, rung,* and *sung.* Use these participles with auxiliaries such as *have, has,* and *had.*

Example 1. The play *began* at eight o'clock.
Example 2. Philip *has come* home early.

It would be incorrect to use "The play begun" in example 1 or "Philip has came" in example 2. "The play has began" and "Philip come home" would also be wrong.

**21b.** The past tenses of the verbs *do, go, eat,* and *see* are *did, went, ate,* and *saw.* These forms should not be used with auxiliaries. The past participles *done, gone, eaten,* and *seen* are used with auxiliary verbs.

Example 1. John *did* all the work yesterday.
Example 2. The girls *have seen* that picture.

It would be incorrect to use "John done all the work" in example 1 or "The girls have saw" in example 2. It would also be incorrect to say "has did" or "The girls seen that picture."

**21c.** The past tenses of the verbs *give, take, write,* and *ride* are *gave, took, wrote,* and *rode.* The past participles are *given, taken, written,* and *ridden.* Use the past tenses alone, and the past participles with auxiliaries.

Example 1. We *took* him to the hospital.
Example 2. That book *was written* before the war.

It would be wrong to use "we taken him" in example 1 or "was wrote" in example 2. "We have took him" would also be wrong.

**21d.** The past tenses of the verbs *grow, know, throw, blow, fly,* and *draw* are *grew, knew, threw, blew, flew,* and *drew.* Never use these forms with auxiliaries, such as *has, had,* or *was.* The past participles are *grown, known, thrown, blown, flown,* and *drawn.* Use these participles with auxiliaries.

Example 1. Mr. Dent *had* never *flown* before.

Example 2. Sally *drew* a sketch for us.

It would be incorrect to use "Mr. Dent had never flew" in example 1 or "Sally drawn" in example 2. "Sally has drew" would also be wrong. There are no such forms as "growed," "knowed," "throwed," "blowed," or "drawed." These are *always* wrong.

**21e.** The past tenses of the verbs *speak, break, freeze, choose,* and *steal* are *spoke, broke, froze, chose,* and *stole.* Never use these forms with auxiliaries. The past participles *spoken, broken, frozen, chosen,* and *stolen* are used with auxiliary verbs.

Example 1. Joe's watch *has been stolen.*

Example 2. I *spoke* to Miss Bolton about you.

It would be incorrect to say "Joe's watch has been stole," or "I spoken to Miss Bolton." "I have spoke" would also be wrong.

**21f.** The past tenses of the verbs *wear, tear,* and *swear* are *wore, tore,* and *swore.* Do not use these forms with auxiliaries. The past participles, *worn, torn,* and *sworn,* are used with auxiliaries.

Example 1. Dick *tore* his trousers on that nail.

Example 2. I *have worn* a hole in my shoe.

It would be incorrect to use "Dick torn" in example 1 or "I have wore" in example 2.

**22. The past tense and the past participle of the verb *bring* are the same word, *brought.* There are no such forms as "brang" and "brung."**

Example 1. Irwin *brought* me these flowers.

Example 2. *Have* you *brought* the money with you?

**23. Do not use the present tense to express past time.**

Example. Then he *ran* and *tried* to catch me, but I was too quick for him.

It would be incorrect to use "he runs and tries" in this sentence, for it is clear that the speaker is telling about what happened at some past time.

**23a.** The words *give, come, eat, says, use, asks,* and *start* are all present tenses; they should not be used for the past tenses *gave, came, ate, said, used, asked,* and *started.*

Example 1. Ellis *gave* me this book for Christmas.

Example 2. Last night he *said* he couldn't go.

Example 3. The mail *came* after four o'clock yesterday.

**24. Use the present perfect or the present perfect progressive tense, not the past or the present progressive, to show action continuing up to the present time.**

Example 1.  We *have written* to Tom every week since he went away.

The word "since" shows that Tom is still away; therefore "we wrote" would be incorrect.

Example 2.  I *have lived* here for ten years.

Example 3.  I *have been living* here for the past ten years.

It would be incorrect to say "I am living here for ten years."

**25. Use the past tense, not the present perfect, for action completed at a definite time in the past.**

Example.  Bob *went* to New York last month.

It would be incorrect to say "Bob has gone to New York last month."

# II.  Choice of the Right Verb

**26.** *Sit* **means** *rest* **or** *occupy a place.* **Except in a few special uses, it is an intransitive verb (15a) and does not take an object.  The principal parts are** *sit, sat, sitting, sat.*  **(See also 26a.)**

Example 1.  Mother told us not to *sit* on the antique chair.

Example 2.  Henry and Martha *sat* behind us at the theater.

Example 3.  The cookie jar *is sitting* on the top shelf.

**26a.** *Set* **means** *put* **or** *place.* **Except in a few special uses, it is a transitive verb (15) and requires an object when it is in the active voice (17, 17a, 17b).  The principal parts are** *set, set, setting, set.*  **(See also 26.)**

Example 1.  Who *set* that vase on the mantel?

Example 2.  *Set* this tray on the small table.

**27.** *Let* **means** *permit.* **The principal parts are** *let, let, letting, let.*  **(See also 27a.)**

Example 1.  *Let* me tie that knot for you.

Example 2.  Mr. Higgins *let* me drive his car yesterday.

It would be incorrect to use "leave" in example 1 or "left" in example 2.

**27a.** *Leave* **means** *go away* **or** *allow to remain.* **The principal parts are** *leave, left, leaving, left.*  **(See also 27.)**

Example 1.  You may *leave* as soon as you are ready.

Example 2.  Henry *left* the window open all night.

**28.** The verb *teach* means to give information or train in some skill. *Learn* means to receive information or acquire some skill.

Example 1.   He *taught* me a great deal about chemistry.
Example 2.   Will you *teach* me to use the slide rule?
Example 3.   Ruth *has learned* the game very quickly.

**29.** *Rise* means *go up, get up,* or *become higher.* It is an intransitive verb (15a). The principal parts are *rise, rose, rising, and risen.*

Example 1.   How much *has* the temperature *risen*?
Example 2.   Anne *rose* from her chair beside the fire.

**29a.** *Raise* means *lift* or *make higher.* It is a transitive verb and takes an object (15, 17, 17a, 17b). The principal parts are *raise, raised, raising, raised.* (See also 29.)

Example 1.   Please *raise* the lid of that box.
Example 2.   Mr. Barnes *has raised* the price of his eggs.

**30.** *Lie* means *rest* or *take a resting position.* It is always intransitive (15a). The principal parts are *lie, lay, lying, lain.* (See also 30a.)

Example 1.   Why don't you *lie* down for a while before dinner?
Example 2.   I *lay* there and waited for someone to come.
Example 3.   Your dog *is lying* in the driveway.
Example 4.   These papers *have lain* on your desk for days.
It would be incorrect to use "lay" in example 1, "laid" in examples 2 or 4, or "laying" in example 3.

**30a.** *Lay* means *put* or *place.* It is always transitive and should not be used without an object or, in the passive voice, a subject that receives the action (15, 17, 17a, 17b). The principal parts are *lay, laid, laying, laid.*

Example 1.   Harry always *lays* his shirts in this drawer.
Example 2.   I *laid* the letter on Miss Carter's desk.
Example 3.   Linoleum *was laid* over the kitchen floor.

**31.** The verb *may* and its past tense, *might,* refer to asking or giving permission, or to possibility or contingency. *Can* and *could* refer to the power or ability to do something. Avoid the use of *can* or *could* where *may* or *might* is required.

Example 1.   *May* I use your pen?
Example 2.   Did Mr. Stone say that he *might* leave early today?
Example 3.   *Can* the new typist take dictation?
Example 4.   He thought he *could* move the trunk without help.

**32.** *Affect* and *effect* are two different verbs, but are sometimes confused. *Affect* means *act upon* or *influence*. *Effect* means *bring about* or *accomplish*. Be sure to use the one that correctly expresses your meaning.

Example 1. The new rule does not *affect* us.

Example 2. Great savings have been *effected* through the new filing system.

**33.** The verb *accept* means to *take when offered*. *Except*, when it is a verb, means to *leave out* or *take out*. Do not use *except* when you mean *accept*.

Example 1. Your report will not be *accepted* unless it is in proper form.

Example 2. Jim must be included, for we cannot *except* anyone.

**34.** *Bring* is used to speak of conveying or carrying a person or thing *to* or *toward* the place where the speaker is or expects to be. *Take* should be used when the motion thought of is away from the speaker or toward some place other than where the speaker is at the time. Do not use *bring* when *take* is required.

Example 1. Bill *brought* his brother here last night.

Example 2. *Take* this blueprint to Mr. Farley's office.

Example 3. We *took* the girls to the movies and afterwards went to Jean's house.

It would be incorrect to use *bring* in example 2 or *brought* in example 3.

**35.** The use of *loan* as a verb instead of *lend* is very general and is acceptable for most speech and writing. In some uses, however, particularly in formal writing, *lend* is usually preferable, unless bank loans or international loans are being discussed.

Example 1. The boy's excited manner *lent* an appearance of truth to his story.

Example 2. The United States Government *loaned* large sums to China.

## III. Agreement of Subject and Verb

**36.** A verb agrees in number (18a) and person (18) with its subject (1). Do not use the singular form of the verb when the subject is plural, or the plural form when the subject is singular.

Example 1. The children *go* to school on the bus.

Example 2. Mr. Williams *wants* to see both of you.

Example 3. Mr. Henson and Dr. Carr *expect* to be there.

It would be incorrect to use "goes" in example 1, "want" in example 2, or "expects" in example 3.

**37. Use *doesn't*, not *don't*, with *he, she, it, this, that*, or a singular noun.**

Example 1.  He *doesn't* like to play golf.

*Doesn't* is a contraction (58) formed by combining the words *does* and *not*.  *Don't* is a contraction of *do not*.  You would not say "He do not." Since *don't* means *do not*, you should not say "He don't."  *Doesn't* is the third person singular form and should therefore be used with the third person singular pronoun *he*.

Example 2.  *Doesn't* Martha work with you?

Example 3.  That *doesn't* matter.

**38. *Are, were, have*, and *do* are plural forms.  They should be used whenever the subject of the verb denotes two or more persons or things.**

Example 1.  John and Betty *have* agreed to help us.

Example 2.  He and his brother *are* at home.

Example 3.  Dixon and I *were* invited to the party.

**38a. The word *you* takes a plural verb whether *you* means one person or more than one.  *We* and *they*, of course, are always plural.  Use *are, were, have*, and *do* after these words.**

Example 1.  You *were* late this morning.

Example 2.  We *weren't* expecting him.

Example 3.  They *were* helping Charles.

Example 4.  *Were* you at the game yesterday?

**39. In sentences beginning with *there is, there are, there was, there were, there has been*, and *there have been*, the word *there* is merely an introductory word.  The subject of the verb comes after it, and the verb should agree in number with this subject.**

Example 1.  There *are* two men waiting to see you.

Example 2.  *Were* there enough sandwiches for everyone?

Example 3.  There *have been* some severe storms lately.

In the examples the subjects, *men, sandwiches*, and *storms*, are all plural and so require plural verbs.  It would be incorrect to use *is, was*, and *has been* in these sentences.

**40. A verb agrees in number with its subject and not with nouns of different number that may occur in phrases modifying the subject.**

**40a. When the subject is the word *one*, the verb is singular. When the subject is *several, a few*, or *many*, the verb is plural.**

Example 1. One of your brothers *was looking* for you.

The simple subject of this sentence is *one,* and the word *brothers* in the phrase modifying it does not affect the verb. It would be wrong to use "were" in this sentence.

Example 2. Several of the coins in that box *are* very rare.

The subject, *several,* is plural, so that it would be incorrect to use "is" in example 2.

**40b. Nouns or pronouns occurring in modifying phrases introduced by such expressions as *along with, together with,* and *as well as* do not affect the number of the verb.**

Example 1. My father, along with the neighbors, *has signed* the petition.

Example 2. The clerks, together with the manager, *are* in favor of the new system.

In example 1 the singular verb *has signed* agrees with the singular subject *father.* In example 2 the plural verb *are* agrees with the plural subject *clerks.*

**41. When the subject of a verb consists of two or more singular words joined by *or,* *either—or,* or *neither—nor,* a singular verb should be used.**

Example 1. Jerry or Phil *has* been using this pen.

Example 2. Either that girl or her sister *works* in Tom's office.

Example 3. Neither the title of the book nor the author's name *is* written clearly.

**41a. When the subject of a verb consists of two or more plural words joined by *or,* *either—or,* or *neither—nor,* use a plural verb. When one of the elements of the subject is plural and the other singular, it is usually better to use a plural verb and place the plural part of the subject next to the verb.**

Example 1. Neither machinists nor electricians *are* needed for this work.

Example 2. Either the engineer or his assistants *make* all the drawings.

**42. Nouns modified by *each, every, either,* and *neither* are singular and require singular verbs. When two or more nouns are modified by such an adjective, they also take a singular verb.**

Example 1. Either applicant *is* a good choice for the job.

Example 2. Neither side *feels* that the decision was fair.

Example 3. Every man, woman, and child *has* been registered.

**42a. The indefinite pronouns, such as *everybody, everyone, each, anyone, either,* and *neither,* require singular verbs.**

Example 1. Each of the girls *wants* to do something to help.

The verb agrees with the singular subject *each* and not with the plural *girls* in the modifying phrase.

Example 2. Neither of the artists *likes* this new design.

Example 3. Everyone in the room *has* passed the examination.

**43. With nouns denoting a group made up of separate persons or things (*collective nouns*), the verb may be singular or plural, depending upon whether the group is thought of as a single unit or as separate individuals. Some such nouns are *jury, audience, crowd, family, cast* (of a play), *crew,* and *majority.***

The choice of a verb in each particular case must depend upon the sense intended rather than upon a fixed rule. The following examples, however, will help to make clear the difference in meaning expressed by a singular or a plural verb.

Example 1. (a) His family *is* a distinguished one.
           (b) Our family all *have* different hobbies.

Example 2. (a) The jury *has* not yet reported a verdict.
           (b) The jury *have* been wrangling for days.

Example 3. (a) A majority of the votes *is* needed for election.
           (b) The majority of the pupils *are* in good health.

**44. Certain expressions of quantity or number may take singular or plural verbs, depending upon the meaning to be expressed. Among these expressions are the words *plenty, variety, rest,* and *number,* and fractions, such as *two thirds* or *one fourth.***

Example 1. (a) Plenty of butter *is* needed for this cake.
           (b) *Are* there plenty of rooms available?

Example 2. (a) A number of girls *have* been employed at the factory.
           (b) The number of replies he received *was* surprising.

Example 3. (a) A variety of interests *is* desirable.
           (b) A variety of different patterns *are* displayed.

Example 4. (a) Two thirds of the land *is* now under water.
           (b) One fourth of the members *live* outside the city.

**45. When a subject consists of two or more parts joined by *and,* a plural verb is used, even though the noun is omitted in one or more parts of the subject.**

Example 1. A black and a brown coat *were* left on the rack.

The word *coat* has been omitted after *black*; two separate coats are meant and the verb is therefore plural.

Example 2. The funniest, the most beautiful, and the most original costume *have* been chosen.

**46. A subject consisting of two singular nouns that refer to the same person or thing, or that are thought of as one, takes a singular verb.**

Example 1. The vice president and general manager *occupies* the corner office.

This sentence refers to one person who is both vice president and general manager.

Example 2. This silence and gloom *is* frightening.

The *silence and gloom* is thought of as a combination, not as two separate things.

**47. Some nouns that appear to be plural because they end in *s* are actually singular in most uses and require singular verbs. Among the most common examples are *mathematics, news, civics, physics,* and *measles.***

Example 1. Civics *was* my favorite subject in high school.

Example 2. Measles *is* not usually a serious disease.

**48. Some nouns have only plural forms and require plural verbs. *Riches, thanks, tongs, trousers,* and *scissors* are among the most commonly used of these nouns.**

Example 1. My scissors *have* been magnetized.

Example 2. Thanks *are* due the women for their help.

**49. An expression indicating a definite amount of money, space of time, or quantity of something takes a singular verb when it is singular in meaning even though plural in form.**

Example 1. Ten dollars *covers* all your expenses for the trip.

Example 2. Two weeks *is* the vacation period allowed by the company.

Example 3. Four yards *seems* more than enough to make a dress like that.

**50. When the subject of a verb is the title of a single book, play, or the like, the verb is singular whether or not the title is plural in form.**

Example 1. Bartlett's *Familiar Quotations has been* famous for many years.

Example 2. *Leaves of Grass is* on the third shelf.

## IV. Verbs in Subordinate Clauses

**51. When the subject of a verb in a modifying clause (11, 224) is *who, which,* or *that,* the verb agrees in number and person with the noun or pronoun modified by the clause.**

Example 1. It is I who *am* always blamed for these errors.

The clause beginning with *who* modifies *I*, which is first person singular. Therefore *am* is used after *who*.

Example 2. Accurate measurement is one of the most important things that *have* to be learned in this work.

The clause beginning with *that* modifies the plural *things,* not "one," and so *have* is used.

Example 3. Mrs. Smith is one of those women who *enjoy* club activities.

The clause introduced by *who* modifies the plural *women,* and *who* is therefore followed by the plural form of the verb. It would be incorrect to use *enjoys* after *who* in this sentence.

**52. When the verb in the principal clause (2) of a sentence is in the past tense, the verb in the subordinate clause is also normally in the past tense. However, when the subordinate clause states a present or permanent fact, its verb should be in the present tense even though the tense of the principal verb is past.**

Example 1. We *ran* to the window when we *heard* the fire engines.

Example 2. I remembered that East St. Louis *is* in Illinois, not in Missouri.

Example 3. William Harvey discovered that the blood *circulates* through the body.

In examples 2 and 3, the clauses introduced by *that* are statements of permanent fact. Therefore the present tenses *is* and *circulates* are used, although the verbs of the main clauses, *remembered* and *discovered,* are in the past tense.

**53. When the verb of the main clause is in the past tense and the subordinate clause is to express action that took place before that of the main verb, the past perfect tense is usually needed in the subordinate clause.**

Example 1. (a) Carl told Helen that his brother *had been* sick.
            (b) Carl told Helen that his brother *was* sick.

In sentence (a), the past perfect *had been* shows that Carl's brother had recovered at the time Carl talked to Helen. In sentence (b), his brother was still sick when Carl talked to Helen.

Example 2. If you *had tried,* you could have won the prize.

This is a *conditional* sentence; neither the trying nor the winning actually took place. But the trying would have had to precede the winning, and so the past perfect is used in the subordinate clause.

**54. Do not use "would have" or "would of" or "had of" in place of *had* in clauses introduced by *if* (conditional clauses).**

Example 1. If you *had done* what I asked, everything would have been all right.

It would be incorrect to say "If you would have done," or "If you would of done," or "If you had of done."

Example 2. The party would have been a success if Barbara *had come*.

**55. In a subordinate clause expressing a wish or a condition that is contrary to fact, use *were* instead of "was."**

Example 1. If I *were* you, I should ask Henry to come.

Obviously the *if* clause states a condition that is not a fact, and so *were* is used and not "was."

Example 2. Dick wishes that he *were* old enough to join the Navy.

Here the clause beginning with *that* expresses a wish.

Example 3. If Mrs. Hale *was* here, why didn't someone call me?

In example 3, the *if* clause expresses a fact that took place at some past time, not a contrary-to-fact condition. Therefore *was* is used.

*Note:* English verbs formerly changed their form when used in conditional or contrary-to-fact statements. Verbs in such uses are said to be in the *subjunctive mode.* The *were* illustrated in examples 1 and 2 is almost the only change of form to show the subjunctive that is of any importance in modern English.

**56. Use the auxiliary *should*, not "would," in the *if* clause of a conditional sentence.**

Example 1. If you *should* decide to come on Sunday, telephone us.

Example 2. If Arthur *should* be transferred to Boston, his family would go with him.

Example 3. If I *should* be delayed, don't wait for me.

**56a. *Would* is used in a conditional *if* clause when it is not merely an auxiliary but expresses willingness or desire to do something.**

Example 1. I could not do that, even if I *would*.

In this sentence "if I would" means "if I wanted to."

Example 2. If Alice would eat the right kinds of food, her health would improve.

In example 2, "If Alice would eat" means "If Alice were willing to eat," and so *would* is correct.

**57. In a clause expressing purpose, such as one introduced by *so that*, use *may, can, shall*, and *will* when the verb of the main clause is in the present, present perfect, or future tense. When the main verb is in a past tense, use *might, could, should*, and *would*.**

**Example 1.** Peter has come early so that he *may* leave before three o'clock.

In this sentence, the present perfect *has come* is followed by *may*. It would be incorrect to use "might" instead of *may* in this sentence.

**Example 2.** Sally always wears a hat so that she *will* not get sunburned.

**Example 3.** The foreman gave the directions clearly in order that there *might* be no misunderstanding.

## V. Some Special Verb Problems

**58. A verb and the word *not* may be combined to form a contraction, such as *don't*, *couldn't*, and *won't*. In writing contractions be sure to insert the apostrophe between *n* and *t*.**

Example. John *can't* find his pen.

It would be incorrect to write "cant," without the apostrophe.

**59. It is never correct to use "ain't" as a contraction for *am not*, *is not*, *are not*, *has not*, or *have not*.**

**Example 1.** I *haven't* been invited. *Am* I *not* supposed to go?

It is correct to use *haven't* or *have not*, but not "ain't," in the first sentence of example 1. It would be wrong to use "ain't" or "aren't" in the second sentence. *Aren't* is the contraction for *are not*, not for *am not*.

**Example 2.** Mary *isn't* ready to go yet.

**Example 3.** *Aren't* those shoes too large?

In examples 2 and 3 the contractions shown may be used, or the full forms *is not* and *are not*.

**60. Do not use "had" or "hadn't" before *ought*. "Had" and "have" are used as auxiliaries only with past participles, and *ought* is not a participle.**

**Example 1.** You *ought* to send Bob a letter of congratulation.

**Example 2.** They *ought not* to expect favors from you.

It would be incorrect to use "had ought" and "hadn't ought" in sentences like these.

**61. Do not use "of" for *have* in expressions like *could have*, *wouldn't have*, *ought to have*, *must have*, and *might have*.**

**Example 1.** I think you *could have* done a better job than he did.

**Example 2.** Someone *ought to have* told Fred.

In speaking rapidly we often say "could've" and "ought to've" as contractions of *could have* and *ought to have*. But "could of," "ought to of," "might of," and the like should never be written.

**62. For the simple future tense, which tells what is going to happen or is likely to happen, use *shall* in the first person and *will* in the second and third persons.   (See also 62a and 62b.)**

Example 1.  I know I *shall* enjoy that book.

Example 2.  You *will* soon be in Kansas.

Example 3.  John *will* be ready in five minutes.

These sentences are simply statements of what the speaker believes will happen. There is no idea of determination on the part of the speaker to bring about the things he states.

**62a.  To express determination, promise, or compulsion use *will* for the first person and *shall* for the second and third persons.  (See also 62.)**

Example 1.  We *will* never stop trying until we succeed.

This sentence expresses determination on the part of the speaker and some other person or persons.

Example 2.  I *will* take the boys to the game.

Here the speaker makes a promise.

Example 3.  You *shall* finish your work before you leave.

In this sentence there is an idea of compulsion or authority.

Example 4.  Mr. Horton says that John *shall* return your money.

This sentence implies that Mr. Horton will take steps to make sure that John returns the money.

**62b.  In asking questions, always use *shall*, not *will*, for the first person.  (See also 62.)**

Example 1.  *Shall* I wait for you?

Example 2.  *Shall* we take our umbrellas?

**62c.  *Should* and *would* correspond to *shall* and *will* and follow the same rules as those given in 62 and 62a for *shall* and *will*.**

Example 1.  I thought we *should* never get here.

Example 2.  I *should* like to hear that record.

Example 3.  Frank was determined that you *should* go with him.

Example 4.  The supervisor intended that Eleanor *should* rewrite the letters.

*Note:* When *should* means "ought to," it is used for all three persons, as in the following sentences: I *should* do that but I don't want to. You *should* never leave that door open. Carl *should* have helped you.

**63. A verb or part of a verb phrase (20) used in one part of a sentence may be understood in another part and need not be inserted if the same form would be correct in both places.**

Example 1. We can and will give two evenings a week to this service.

Here *give* is correctly understood after *can*.

Example 2. He always has *done* and will continue to do what he thinks is right.

It would be incorrect to say, "He always has and will continue to do what he thinks is right." The past participle *done* is required after *has* and cannot properly be omitted in a sentence like this.

**64. Do not add *ed* to the verbs *burst*, *cast*, *forecast*, or *recast*. These verbs, like *hurt*, *put*, and a few others, have the same form for the present, past, and past participle.**

*Note:* *Broadcasted* may be used in referring to radio broadcasting. In other meanings of *broadcast* the *ed* is not used.

Example 1. The water pipes in our house *burst* last winter.

Example 2. Florence *cast* her first vote last November.

Example 3. Higher temperatures have been *forecast* for tomorrow.

**65. The perfect infinitive (*to have done*, etc.) should not be used after a verb in the past conditional tense (*would have known*, etc.).**

Example 1. David *would have known* what *to say* if he had been there.

The present infinitive *to say* is used in this sentence. It would be incorrect to say "David would have known what to have said."

Example 2. Mrs. Hill *would have liked to be* a teacher.

In a sentence like this it would be incorrect to say "would have liked to have been."

Example 3. I was glad *to have finished* my work on time.

Here the perfect infinitive is correctly used, because the finishing preceded the being glad.

**66. Do not overuse the word *got*, especially in formal writing.**

Example 1. Have you *got* the things I sent you for?

Here *got* is permissible. The sentence means "Have you secured or obtained the things?"

Example 2. His hand *was* hurt when the pile of books fell on it.

In a sentence like this, "got hurt" is inappropriate for formal speech or writing.

Example 3. I *have* three dollars that I can lend you.

Example 4. I *have* to go to that meeting tonight.

The use of "I've got" instead of *I have* in sentences like examples 3 and 4 is frequent in everyday conversation, but should be avoided in more formal speech and in writing.

# NOUNS AND PRONOUNS

Nouns and pronouns perform various functions in sentences, and a noun or pronoun is said to be in one of three *cases* according to the function it performs in a particular sentence.

**67. A noun or pronoun may be the subject (1) of a verb. When it is, it is in the *nominative case*.**

Example 1.  The *boy* rode his bicycle.

Example 2.  *He* lives on Maple Street.

The noun *boy* is the subject of the verb *rode* and the pronoun *he* is the subject of the verb *lives*.

**68. A noun or pronoun may be the *direct object* of a verb (17a), the *indirect object* of a verb, or the *object* of a preposition (10).   A noun or pronoun used as an object is in the *objective case*.**

Example 1.  Has anyone seen *John*?

The noun *John* is the direct object of the verb *has seen*.

Example 2.  Elsie gave *him* a book.

The pronoun *him* is the indirect object of the verb *gave*.   An indirect object denotes the person or thing indirectly affected by the action of the verb.   In example 2, *book* is the direct object of *gave*.

**69. When two or more nouns or pronouns are subjects or objects of the same verb or objects of the same preposition, the subject or object is said to be *compound*.**

Example 1.  *She* and *Albert* came in together.

*She and Albert* is the compound subject.

Example 2.  *Tom* or *Bill* will help you.

Example 3.  Mr. Holmes promoted *Leonard*, *Smith*, and *Thomas*.

**70. A noun or pronoun may be placed beside another that denotes the same person or thing in order to emphasize or explain it.   Such a noun or pronoun is said to be in *apposition* with the word it explains or emphasizes, and is called an *appositive*. An appositive is in the same case as the word with which it is in apposition.**

Example 1.  *Carter*, the *foreman*, has recommended some changes.

The noun *foreman* is in apposition with *Carter*.

Example 2.  You should not say that to *her*, the *sister* of your best friend.

The noun *sister* is in apposition with the pronoun *her*.

**71. A noun or pronoun used after *is, are, was,* or some other form of the verb *to be* (except the infinitive itself) to complete its**

meaning is in the nominative case and is called a *predicate nominative*. Special rules govern the case of the pronoun with the infinitive (86, 86a).

Example 1. Sterling was a good *pilot*.

Example 2. It was *she* who rang the doorbell.

**72. A noun or pronoun used to show ownership, authorship, or some other special relationship to another noun is in the *possessive case*.**

Example 1. Where are *Harry's* gloves?

Example 2. Margaret has promised to bring *her* brother.

Example 3. He never tired of listening to *Beethoven's* music.

**73. Nouns and pronouns denoting one person or thing are *singular* in *number*. Those denoting more than one are *plural*. The principal ways of forming plurals of nouns are given below. When there is doubt as to the spelling of a particular plural, a dictionary should be consulted.**

**73a.** The plurals of nouns are regularly formed by adding *s* or *es* to the singular:

| | | |
|---|---|---|
| *girl — girls* | *box — boxes* | *glass — glasses* |
| *plate — plates* | *belief — beliefs* | *chief — chiefs* |

**73b.** The plurals of some nouns ending in *f* or *fe* are formed by changing the *f* to *ves*:

| | | |
|---|---|---|
| *leaf — leaves* | *wife — wives* | *shelf — shelves* |

**73c.** Some nouns have special forms for the plural:

| | | |
|---|---|---|
| *man — men* | *woman — women* | *child — children* |
| *foot — feet* | *tooth — teeth* | *ox — oxen* |

**73d.** A few nouns have the same form in the plural as in the singular: *deer, trout, sheep.*

**73e.** Some Latin, Greek, and other foreign words commonly used in English retain their foreign plurals:

| | |
|---|---|
| *memorandum — memoranda* | *analysis — analyses* |
| *parenthesis — parentheses* | *alumnus — alumni* |

**74. Pronouns are classified as follows:**

personal pronouns: *I, you, he, she, it, we, they*

relative pronouns: *who, which, that*

indefinite pronouns: *any, each, either, neither, anyone, someone, everybody, no one, nobody, both*

interrogative pronouns: *who, what, which*

demonstrative pronouns: *this, that, these, those*

intensive or reflexive (compound personal) pronouns: *myself, yourself, himself, herself, itself, ourselves, yourselves, themselves*

**75. The personal pronouns are of the first, second, and third persons (18). They and the relative pronoun *who* have different forms for the nominative and objective cases.**

|  | *Personal Pronouns* |  |  | *Relative* |
|---|---|---|---|---|
|  | First Person | Second Person | Third Person |  |
| *Nominative* |  |  |  |  |
| Singular | *I* | *you* | *he, she, it* | *who* |
| Plural | *we* | *you* | *they* | *who* |
| *Objective* |  |  |  |  |
| Singular | *me* | *you* | *him, her, it* | *whom* |
| Plural | *us* | *you* | *them* | *whom* |
| *Possessive* |  |  |  |  |
| Singular | *my, mine* | *your, yours* | *his, her, hers, its* | *whose* |
| Plural | *our, ours* | *your, yours* | *their, theirs* | *whose* |

*Note:* Nouns have the same form for the nominative and objective cases, changing their form only for the possessive case. Rules regarding the possessives of nouns and pronouns begin with rule 100.

**76. The word or group of words to which a pronoun refers or for which it stands is its *antecedent*.**

Example 1. Sally called Frank, but *he* did not hear.

The antecedent of *he* is the noun *Frank*.

Example 2. Miss Burt congratulated everybody *who* took part in the play.

The antecedent of *who* is the indefinite pronoun *everybody*.

# I. Case of Pronouns

**77. A pronoun that is the subject (1) or part of the compound subject (69) of a verb is in the nominative case (75). Do not use the objective form of a pronoun as the subject of a verb.**

Example 1. Bob and *she* went to the beach.

It would be incorrect to use "Bob and her" in this sentence because "her" is the objective form and should not be used as the subject of a verb.

Example 2. *He* and *I* played tennis.

If you have difficulty in using pronouns correctly in compound subjects, test each part of the subject in this way:

(a) *He* played tennis. (b) *I* played tennis. (c) *He* and *I* played tennis.

You would not use "him" for *he* in sentence (a) nor "me" for *I* in sentence (b). It would be just as incorrect to say "him and me" or "me and him" in sentence (c).

**77a. When one part of a compound subject is *I* or *we*, it should be placed after the other part or parts of the subject. If one part of the subject is *you*, it should be placed first.**

Example 1. *You, your brother,* and *I* can go in my car.

Example 2. *Walter* and *I* have been swimming.

**77b. When a pronoun is in the predicate nominative (71) after *is* or some other form of the verb *to be*, use the nominative form (75).**

Example 1. It was *she* who wrote that letter.

Example 2. I thought it was *he* that designed the new model.

*Note:* In everyday conversation this rule is often disregarded, especially in the first person. The rule is followed, however, in more formal speech and writing.

Example 1. Who's at the door? It's *me.*

Example 2. Mr. Gordon was mistaken when he said that it was *I* who compiled the list.

**78. Never use *them* as the subject (1) of a verb. *Them* is the objective form (75) of the pronoun and should never be used where a nominative form is required.**

Example 1. *They* are the boys who broke the window.

Example 2. *Those* are my best shoes.

It would be wrong to use "them" in place of either *they* in example 1 or the demonstrative pronoun *those* in example 2.

**79. A pronoun that is used as the direct object (17a) or part of the compound object of a verb is in the objective case (75). Do not use the nominative form of the pronoun as the object of a verb.**

Example 1. Charles saw *him* on Michigan Avenue.

Example 2. The police questioned Henry and *me* about the accident.

If you are in doubt as to the form of the pronoun that should be used, test each part of the sentence as follows:

(a) The police questioned *Henry.* (b) The police questioned *me.*
(c) The police questioned *Henry* and *me.*

You would not use "I" in sentence (b). It would be just as wrong to use "I" instead of *me* in sentence (c).

Example 3. The Turners have invited *her* and *me* to their party.

**80. A pronoun used as the indirect object (68) or part of a compound (69) indirect object of a verb is in the objective case (75).**

Example 1.  My mother gave *me* this locket.

The pronoun *me* is the indirect object of the verb *gave*. It shows to whom the locket was given. The nominative form "I" would be incorrect in this sentence.

Example 2.  Mr. Franklin will tell *them* or their helpers where the material is.

*Them or their helpers* is the indirect object of *will tell*. The clause *where the material is* is the direct object.

Example 3.  Uncle Harry brought *her* and *me* these rings.

**81. A pronoun used as the object or part of the compound object of a preposition (10) is in the objective case (75).**

Example 1.  Do you want to go with *her?*

The pronoun *her* is the object of the preposition *with* and is in the objective case.

Example 2.  The money was collected by *them* and *us*.

*Them* and *us* are objects of the preposition *by*.

Example 3.  The interview was interesting to both *him* and *me*.

It would be incorrect to use "he" or "I" in place of *him* or *me* as object of the preposition *to* in this sentence.

**81a.** *Except, between,* and *but* (when it means *except*) are prepositions.  Pronouns used as their objects (10) should be in the objective case (75).  (See also 81.)

Example 1.  Everyone is here except *her*.

The objective *her* is used after the preposition *except*.

Example 2.  This work is to be divided between *you* and *me*.

It is incorrect to say "between you and I."

Example 3.  We have met everyone but *him* and his brother.

**81b. The word *like* in some uses functions as a preposition. In such cases a pronoun following *like* should be in the objective, not the nominative, case (75).**

Example 1.  I wish I knew more girls like *her*.

It would be incorrect to use "she" instead of *her* in this sentence.

Example 2.  Like *you* and *me*, John has always wanted to be an engineer.

It would be incorrect to say "like you and I."

*Note:* The same rule applies to *unlike* when it is used as a preposition.

Example.  Unlike *me*, Larry enjoys long hikes.

**82. Use the nominative case (75) for a pronoun that is the subject (1) of a verb and has a noun in apposition (70) with it, or that is in apposition with the noun subject of a verb.**

Example 1. *We* girls wanted to go with them.

Do not say "Us girls wanted to go." The pronoun is the subject, and the nominative *we* is therefore required. You would not use "us" if *girls* were omitted and the sentence read, *We wanted to go with them.* You should therefore not use "us" when *girls* is placed in apposition with the subject.

Example 2. The winners, *he* and *I*, will share the prize money.

The pronouns are in apposition with the noun *winners*, which is the subject of the verb. Therefore the nominative forms *he* and *I* are used.

**82a. Use the objective case (75) for a pronoun that is the direct or indirect (68) object of a verb and has a noun in apposition (70) with it, or that is in apposition with the direct or indirect object of a verb.**

Example 1. The fire chief thanked *us* boys for helping him.

The objective form *us* is used because the pronoun is the object of the verb *thanked*. It would be incorrect to say "thanked we boys."

Example 2. They gave *us* new employees careful instructions.

In example 2, *us* is used because the pronoun is the indirect object of the verb *gave*. The noun *employees* is in apposition with the pronoun *us*.

Example 3. Paul will need two assistants, Harry and *me*, on this job.

The noun *Harry* and the pronoun *me* are in apposition with *assistants*, the object of the verb *will need*. The objective form *me* is therefore used.

**82b. Use the objective case (75) for a pronoun that is the object of a preposition (10) and has a noun in apposition (70) with it, or that is in apposition with the object of a preposition.**

Example 1. In a few days there will be new equipment for *us* men.

Example 2. Mr. Cole left the farm to his two oldest children, Edward and *her*.

The noun *Edward* and the pronoun *her* are in apposition with *children*, the object of the preposition *to*. The objective *her* is therefore used.

Example 3. What did he say about *us*, Alice and *me*?

In example 3, *Alice* and *me* are in apposition with *us*, which is the object of the preposition *about*, and so the objective form *me* is used.

**83. The conjunction (12) *than* and the conjunctive adverb *as* are used to join two clauses that state a comparison. Often, however, the second clause is implied rather than stated in full and *than* is followed only by a pronoun. The case (75) of the**

**pronoun is the same as that of the word in the first clause with which the pronoun is compared.**

Example 1.  You always drive faster than *I*.

If the comparison were stated in full, the sentence would be *You always drive faster than I drive.* The comparison is between *you*, which is the subject of *drive*, and *I*, which would be the subject of *drive* if the verb were repeated in the second clause. Therefore the nominative case of the pronoun is used.

Example 2.  Henry would rather take you than *her* on this trip.

If the comparison were stated in full, the sentence would be *Henry would rather take you than he would take her.* The word with which *than* compares something is *you*, which is the object of the verb *take*. The objective form *her* is therefore used.

Example 3.  Mrs. Allen paid Frank more than *I*.

The use of the nominative *I* shows that this sentence means *Mrs. Allen paid Frank more than I paid him.*

Example 4.  Mrs. Allen paid Frank more than *me*.

The use of the objective *me* shows that this sentence means *Mrs. Allen paid Frank more than she paid me.*

**84.  The relative pronouns *who*, *which*, and *that* are used to introduce subordinate clauses (2, 11).  The case of a relative pronoun is determined by the function it performs in the subordinate clause, and not by the function of its antecedent (76) in the main clause.  *That* and *which* have no other forms to indicate case, but *who* has the objective form *whom*.**

**84a.** The nominative (75) form *who* is used when the relative pronoun is the subject (1) of the clause it introduces. (See also 84.)

Example 1.  George knows a man *who* has just come from Australia.

The subordinate clause is *who has just come from Australia.* The nominative form *who* is used because the relative pronoun is the subject of the verb *has come*.

Example 2.  I voted for the man *who* I thought had the best qualifications.

It would be incorrect to use "whom" in this sentence. The relative pronoun is not the object of *thought* but the subject of *had*. Therefore the nominative form *who* is needed.  *I thought* is a parenthetical expression which could be omitted without affecting the grammatical completeness of the clause.

**84b.** The objective (75) form *whom* is used when the relative pronoun is the object of a verb (17a) or of a preposition (10).

Example 1.  Mr. MacNeil, *whom* I met in New England, has come to visit us.

The subordinate clause is *whom I met in New England.* The relative pronoun is the object of the verb *met* and *whom* is therefore the correct form.

Example 2.  The officer to *whom* your letter was addressed is no longer here.

The subordinate clause is *to whom your letter was addressed.* The relative pronoun is the object of the preposition *to,* and so the objective *whom* is used.

**84c.  *Whoever* differs from the relative pronoun *who* in two ways.  It means *anyone who* and thus does not require an antecedent (76), while *who* always refers to a noun or pronoun in the sentence.  The other difference is that a clause (2) introduced by *whoever* may be the subject of a verb, the direct or indirect object of a verb, or the object of a preposition, while a clause introduced by *who* modifies a noun or a pronoun.  The case of *whoever* is determined by its function in the clause it introduces and not by the function of the entire clause in the sentence.**

Example 1.  They will appoint *whoever* makes the highest score.

The object of the verb *will appoint* is not *whoever* but the entire clause introduced by *whoever.* The relative pronoun is the subject of this clause; therefore the nominative form *whoever* is needed.

Example 2.  We are sure that *whomever* you send will be a capable person.

In example 2 the relative pronoun introduces the clause *whomever you send.* *Whomever* is the object of the verb *send* and the objective form is therefore used.

*Note*:  In ordinary speech and writing *whomever* is rarely used.  We should probably say, "*Whoever* you send will be welcome." In formal writing, however, the distinction is observed and *whomever* used when it is the grammatically accurate form.

**84d.  Do not use *whomever* as the subject of a clause.**

Example 1.  Stop *whoever* tries to enter that gate.

Example 2.  I will give this work to *whoever* you think can do it.

Some people wrongly use "whomever" in sentences like these.  In example 1 *whoever* is the subject of *tries.* In example 2 *whoever* is the subject of *can do* and its case is not affected by the insertion of *you think.*

**85.  The interrogative pronoun *who* and its objective form *whom* are used to introduce questions.  When the interrogative pronoun is the subject of a verb, the nominative *who* is used.**

**When it is the object of a verb or a preposition, the objective *whom* is used.**

Example 1. *Who* do you think he is?

By transposing this question to "You do think he is who," we see that the interrogative pronoun is not the object of *think* but the predicate nominative (71) after *is*. The nominative *who* is therefore correct.

Example 2. *Who* did you say brought these apples?

Example 3. *Whom* shall we invite to dinner?

*Whom* is the object of the verb *shall invite*.

Example 4. *Whom* should this be sent to?

*Whom* is the object of the preposition *to*.

*Note*: In the everyday speech of most people the interrogative *whom* is seldom used. We say: *Who are the flowers for? Who did you see? Who are you talking about?* In formal speech and in writing, however, *whom* is used when it is grammatically correct, as in the following examples:

*Whom* should the voters hold responsible for this neglect of the public welfare?

For *whom* is there any advantage in this procedure?

**86. The pronoun following *to be* is in the objective case when the infinitive (19a) *to be* links the pronoun to a noun or another pronoun in the objective case (75).**

Example 1. They believed him to be *me*.

To agree with the objective *him*, *me* is used and not **I**.

Example 2. I expected it to be *him*.

**86a. When the infinitive *to be* has no subject, the pronoun following *to be* is in the nominative case.**

Example. He was thought to be *I*.

As *to be* has no subject, the following pronoun is in the nominative case. See also 86, example 1.

## II. Agreement of Pronoun and Antecedent

**87. A pronoun agrees with its antecedent (76) in number and person (75).**

Example 1. Mary said *she* would come over.

Example 2. Ask Fred and Bob to take you with *them*.

In example 1, the antecedent of *she* is *Mary,* which is third person singular. The third person singular pronoun is therefore used, and the feminine form *she* is chosen because *Mary* is the name of a woman or a girl. In example 2, the antecedent of *them* is *Fred and Bob,* and so the third person plural pronoun is required.

**88. A pronoun whose antecedent (76) is a singular indefinite pronoun, such as *anyone*, *everyone*, *everybody*, *each*, *either*, *neither*, *someone*, *no one*, and *nobody*, is in the third person singular. The masculine form (*he*, *him*, *his*) is used when the reference is to persons, unless the sentence makes clear that only women or girls are involved.**

Example 1. Does each of the typewriters have *its* cover on?

Example 2. Has anyone lost *his* keys?

Example 3. Neither of the boys would admit that *he* was the offender.

The third person singular pronouns *its*, *his*, and *he* are used because the antecedents *each*, *anyone*, and *neither* are third person singular. It would be incorrect to say, "Does each of the typewriters have their cover on?" or "Has anyone lost their keys?" or "Neither of the boys would admit that they were the offender."

Example 4. The girls marched in and each took *her* place on the platform.

In this sentence it is clear that *each* must mean "each girl," and so the feminine *her* is used after *each*.

Example 5. Everybody is to come to this desk and write *his* name on the list.

It would be incorrect to use "your" or "their" instead of *his* in this sentence, because *everybody* must be followed by the third person singular.

**89. A pronoun whose antecedent (76) is a noun or nouns modified by one of the indefinite adjectives *each*, *every*, *either*, and *neither* is in the third person singular.**

Example 1. Either child will do that if you ask *him*.

Example 2. Every car and truck must have *its* inspection sticker on the windshield.

Example 3. Each person will have a locker for *his* personal belongings.

**90. When a pronoun refers to two or more singular words joined by *or*, the pronoun is singular.**

Example 1 Dale or James will lend you *his* bicycle.

Example 2. Mrs. Fenton or Mrs. Brooks left *her* gloves in the car.

**91. When the word *one* is used as an indefinite pronoun, pronouns referring to it may be either *one* (*one's*) or *he* (*him*, *his*), but not "they" or "you."**

Example 1. One cannot do *one's* best work under such conditions.

*His* might be used in place of *one's*, but "their" or "your" would be wrong.

Example 2. One would not mind the delay if *he* knew there was a good reason for it.

*One* might be used in place of *he,* but "you" or "they" should not be used.

**92. When the antecedent of a pronoun is a collective noun (43), the pronoun may be singular or plural, depending upon whether the group is thought of as a single unit or as separate individuals.**

Example 1.    The crew went to the lifeboats assigned to *them.*

Example 2.    The graduating class have invited *their* friends to the class-day exercises.

In examples 1 and 2 the members of the crew and the class are thought of as separate individuals acting separately. Therefore *them* and *their* are used. Notice that in example 2 the plural verb *have invited* is consistent with the plural pronoun. It would be incorrect to say "The class has invited their friends" or "The class have invited its friends."

Example 3.    Our committee made *its* report last Monday.

Here the committee acts as a unit and so the singular pronoun is used.

**93. Do not use the relative pronoun *which* to refer to persons. *Who* is used when referring to persons and sometimes to animals that are given individual names, such as pets. *Which* is used to refer to animals, things, and ideas. *That* may refer to persons, animals, things, or ideas. If the pronoun refers to a person and an animal or thing, use *that.***

Example 1.    The man *who* wants to win an election must have friends.

It would be incorrect to use "which" instead of *who* in this sentence.

Example 2.    The monkey *which* was the favorite of visitors to the zoo has just died.

In examples 1 and 2, *that* might be used instead of *who* or *which.*

Example 3.    Everyone was praising the boy and the dog *that* discovered the fire.

Since the clause, *that discovered the fire,* modifies *the boy and the dog,* neither *who* nor *which* could be used in place of *that.*

**93a. Do not use *what* as a relative pronoun after an antecedent (76) that is expressed. Use *who, that,* or *which.***

Example 1.    There is no one here *who* can tell you.

Example 2.    Where is the pen *that* you had yesterday?

It would be incorrect to use "what" in place of *who* or *that* in these sentences.

Example 3.    Show Jim *what* you have found.

Here *what* is correctly used. As a relative pronoun *what* has the meaning *that which* or *those things which.* It would therefore be incorrect to say, "Show Jim the things what you have found."

## III. Miscellaneous Pronoun Problems

**94. The relative pronoun *which* is used to introduce a subordinate clause (2) and must itself have a function, as subject or object of a verb, or object of a preposition, in the subordinate clause. It should *not* be used instead of *and* or *but* to join two independent clauses.**

Example 1. I tried on four hats, *but* I didn't like any of them.

It would be incorrect to say "which I didn't like any of them," as *which* would have no function in such a clause.

Example 2. The children went to the beach, *and* they all had a very good time.

It would be wrong to use "which" instead of *and* in this sentence.

**95. Do not repeat a noun subject by needlessly using a personal pronoun subject just after it.**

Example 1. The sheriff captured the thief.

It would be incorrect to say "The sheriff he captured the thief."

Example 2. Dan and Joe want us to go with them.

It would be incorrect to say "Dan and Joe they want us to go."

**96. The compound personal pronouns are *myself, yourself, himself, herself, itself, ourselves, yourselves,* and *themselves.* They are used for emphasis, and as the objects of verbs or prepositions when the object refers back to the subject of the sentence or clause. The first use is called the *intensive*; the second the *reflexive.* There are no such forms as "hisself," "theirself," or "theirselves."**

Example 1. I *myself* have often seen that happen.

Example 2. You said the same thing *yourself.*

Example 3. Jack has hurt *himself.*

Example 4. The children kept some of the candy for *themselves.*

Example 5. His record will speak for *itself.*

**96a. A compound personal pronoun (96) should not be used as a substitute for the nominative (67, 75) form of a simple pronoun.**

Example 1. My brother and *I* were born in Atlanta.

You would not say "Myself was born in Atlanta." It is equally incorrect to say, "My brother and myself were born in Atlanta."

Example 2. Thompson said that neither *he* nor the other watchman had heard anything.

It would be incorrect to substitute "himself" for *he* in this sentence.

**97. The word "same" should not be used as a pronoun to take the place of *it*, *they*, or *them*.**

Example 1. We have received your letter and wish to thank you for *it*.

Example 2. Two of the books are damaged. We are returning *them* by parcel post.

"Same" or "the same" should not be used in place of *it* and *them* in sentences like these.

**98. The pronoun *it* should not be used without an antecedent (76), expressed or understood, except when it serves merely as an introductory word for the true subject following the verb, or in such expressions as *it is raining* or *it snowed*.**

Example 1. This book tells about the national parks.

The use of expressions like "It tells about the national parks in this book" should be avoided, especially in writing.

Example 2. *It* is unfortunate that you cannot go.

This sentence means *That you cannot go is unfortunate*. The clause, *that you cannot go,* is the true subject of the sentence (225), and *it* is merely an introductory word. This use of *it* is entirely correct.

**99. Avoid the use of *they* without an antecedent (76).**

Example 1. There was a big fire in the lumberyard yesterday.

Example 2. Steel is made in Youngstown.

Expressions like "They had a big fire in the lumberyard" and "They make steel in Youngstown," while not objectionable in everyday conversation, should not be used in writing or in more formal speech.

## IV. Possessives

**100. The possessive case (72) of a singular noun is formed by adding an apostrophe and *s* ('*s*) to the noun.**

Example 1. The tall *man's* name is Coleman.

Example 2. We have looked at Mrs. *Dodge's* report.

Example 3. Mr. *Jones's* advice is usually good.

Example 4. We have just received *Charles's* picture.

*Note*: In some cases of singular nouns of more than one syllable, ending in *s,* the possessive may be formed by adding only the apostrophe. This is sometimes done to avoid awkward pronunciation that would be required if the *s* were added as well as the apostrophe. For example, we may write *Mr. Parsons' letter.*

**100a. To form the possessive case (72) of a plural noun ending in *s*, add an apostrophe only, after the *s* that forms the plural.**

Example 1. Mrs. Hart sells *girls'* clothing.
Example 2. The *thieves'* fingerprints were found on the door.

**100b.** To form the possessive case (72) of a plural noun not ending in *s*, use an apostrophe and *s* ('s).

Example 1. The *men's* working hours are from eight to five.
Example 2. The *children's* parents have been asked to call for them.

**101. To form the possessive case (72) of compound nouns or titles like *brother-in-law* or *Secretary of the Navy*, add the apostrophe and *s* to the last word of the compound (or add the apostrophe alone if the last word is a plural ending in *s*).**

Example 1. She is staying at her *mother-in-law's* house.
Example 2. The *Secretary of State's* speech was loudly applauded.
Example 3. Where is the *Chief of Engineers'* office?

*Note:* Sometimes when a compound name or title is very long, it is better to use a phrase introduced by *of* than a possessive form. "The president of the American Society of Mechanical Engineers' report" is awkward. *The report of the president of the American Society of Mechanical Engineers* should be used instead.

**101a.** When two or more persons are thought of as a single combination possessing something, the possessive case (72) is formed by adding the apostrophe and *s* to the last noun only (or by adding the apostrophe alone if the last noun is a plural ending in *s*).

Example 1. I like to buy at *Warren and Forrest's* dress shop.
Example 2. *Bill and Ruth's* house is on Glenwood Road.

**101b.** When two or more persons are thought of as each separately possessing something, each of the nouns naming the persons is in the possessive case. (See also 101a.)

Example 1. *Carl's* and his *brother's* school records have been excellent.
Example 2. Henry takes care of the *Marvins'* and the *Smiths'* gardens.

**102. The possessive forms of the personal pronouns (75) and the possessive form *whose* are written *without* the apostrophe.**

Example 1. I don't know whether the responsibility is *ours* or *theirs*.
Example 2. If the book is not *yours*, it must be *hers*.
Example 3. *Whose* sailboat was damaged?
Example 4. *Its* value is far less than he claims.

**102a.** The possessive case (72) of an indefinite pronoun followed by *else* (for example, *somebody else*) is formed by adding an apostrophe and *s* to the *else*.

Example 1.   He is never interested in *anybody else's* problems.
Example 2.   I took *someone else's* coat by mistake.

**103. As a general rule, nouns denoting things without life should not be used in the possessive form (100). Use a phrase introduced by *of* instead.**

Example.   The *door of the garage* is unlocked.
Do not say "the garage's door."
There are a number of exceptions to this rule, particularly expressions denoting time, value, or distance, and expressions in which there is an idea of personification.   Some examples are the following: *a day's work, a dollar's worth, an hour's drive, the wind's fury, war's destruction, duty's call.*

**104. The possessive case (72) of a noun or a pronoun is used before a gerund (19a) to indicate the doer of the action named by the gerund.**

Example 1.   What does your father think of *your* going to California?
Example 2.   We were annoyed by *their* trying to deceive us.
Example 3.   Is there any danger of *his* falling off that ledge?
Example 4.   Mrs. Williams was surprised at *my* being in Chicago.
Example 5.   *Martin's* resigning his position creates a problem for us.

## ADJECTIVES AND ADVERBS

**105. The adjectives (8) *this, that, these,* and *those* are used to point out, rather than to describe. They are called *demonstrative adjectives. This* and *that* modify singular nouns. *These* and *those* modify plural nouns.**

Example 1.   *This* coat is too long.
Example 2.   *That* car needs new spark plugs.
Example 3.   Henry doesn't like *these* apples.
Example 4.   Will you lend me *those* books?

**106. The words *a, an,* and *the* are adjectives of a special kind. These words are often called *articles.***

106a.  *A* and *an* usually indicate any person or thing rather than a specific one. They are called *indefinite articles.*

Example 1.   Frank never wears *a* hat.
Example 2.   Don't you want *an* orange?

106b.  The word *the* indicates a particular person or thing, or particular persons or things. It is called the *definite article.*

Example.   *The* boys didn't go to *the* game.

**107. Many adverbs are formed by adding the letters *ly* to adjectives, as in the following examples.**

| *Adjectives* | *Adverbs* |
|---|---|
| careful | carefully |
| happy | happily |
| quiet | quietly |
| comfortable | comfortably |
| shy | shyly |

Note the spelling of *happily* and *comfortably*. When *ly* is added to an adjective of more than one syllable ending in *y*, the *y* is changed to *i*. When the adjective ends in silent *e*, the *e* is dropped.

**107a. Some adverbs have the same form as adjectives.** Among these are *fast, hard, early,* and *first.*

Example 1. The sun rises *early* in summer.

Example 2. You can catch the *early* train if you hurry.

In example 1 *early* is an adverb modifying the verb *rises*. In example 2 *early* is an adjective modifying the noun *train*.

**108. Adjectives have different forms to show different degrees of the quality expressed. The simple adjective itself is called the *positive* degree. The form that indicates a greater measure of the quality as compared with something is called the *comparative* degree. The form that indicates the greatest measure of the quality is called the *superlative* degree.**

The following sentences illustrate the three degrees:

Bob is an *efficient* worker. (positive)

Frank is *more efficient* than Stewart. (comparative)

Tom is the *most efficient* worker we have. (superlative)

**108a. The comparative degree of most short adjectives is made by adding *er* to the positive form and the superlative degree is formed by adding *est* to the positive.**

| *Positive* | *Comparative* | *Superlative* |
|---|---|---|
| long | longer | longest |
| wide | wider | widest |
| happy | happier | happiest |

Notice that when the adjective ends in *e*, only *r* and *st* are added rather than *er* and *est*, and that when the adjective ends in *y*, the *y* is changed to *i* before the *er* or *est* is added.

**108b. The comparative degree of most adjectives of two or more syllables is made by using the word *more* with the posi-**

tive form. The superlative degree is made by using *most* with the positive.

| | | |
|---|---|---|
| interesting | more interesting | most interesting |
| useful | more useful | most useful |

**108c.** Some adjectives form the comparative and the superlative by a change in the word itself. These are said to be irregular, since they do not follow either of the rules for making comparatives and superlatives.

| | | |
|---|---|---|
| good | better | best |
| bad | worse | worst |
| many | more | most |
| little | less | least |

**109. Adverbs also have comparative and superlative degrees. These are regularly formed by using *more* and *most* with the positive adverb form.**

| | | |
|---|---|---|
| quickly | more quickly | most quickly |
| easily | more easily | most easily |

**109a.** A few irregular adverbs have special forms for the comparative and the superlative, and adverbs that have the same form as adjectives have the same comparatives and superlatives as the adjectives.

| | | |
|---|---|---|
| well | better | best |
| badly | worse | worst |
| fast | faster | fastest |

## I. Confusion of Adjectives and Adverbs

**110. Be sure to use the adverb, ending in *ly*, rather than the adjective, when the word to be modified is a verb, an adjective, or an adverb.**

Example 1. Don't talk *foolishly*.

Example 2. Mary is *considerably* taller than her sister.

Example 3. The minutes passed *terribly* slowly as they waited.

It would be incorrect to use the adjectives "foolish," "considerable," and "terrible" in these sentences.

Example 4. I can find the place *more easily* than you.

*More easily* modifies the verb *can find*. It would be incorrect to use the adjective "easier" in this sentence.

*Note*: There are a few adjectives that end in *ly*, such as *lovely*, *friendly*, and *lonely*. Do not use these adjectives as adverbs.

**111.** *Good* **is an adjective;** *well,* **except when it means** *in good health,* **is an adverb. Do not use "good" for** *well* **to modify a verb.**

Example 1. We thought Carl spoke very *well.*

Example 2. Dorothy doesn't play *well.*

**112.** *Sure* **is an adjective;** *surely* **is an adverb. Do not use "sure" when an adverb is needed.**

Example 1. I *surely* wish I could go with you.

Example 2. Everyone *certainly* was glad to see Fred.

It would be incorrect to use "sure" instead of *surely* or *certainly* in these sentences.

**113.** *Real* **is an adjective;** *really* **is an adverb. Do not use "real" for the adverbs** *very* **or** *extremely* **or** *especially.*

Example 1. The children had a *very* good time at the party.

Example 2. Yesterday was an *extremely* hot day.

Example 3. Mr. Cole is *really* worried about his son.

It would be incorrect to use "real" in any of these sentences. *Really* should be used when the meaning is *actually* or *in truth*, as it is in example 3.

**114. Use** *almost,* **not "most," when the meaning is** *nearly.*

Example 1. *Almost* all boys like this book.

Example 2. Are you *almost* ready?

**115.** *Some* **is an adjective. Do not use "some" to modify a verb, an adjective, or an adverb.**

Example 1. The boys worked *somewhat* faster than the girls.

Example 2. He was *much* disappointed in the result.

It would be incorrect to use "some" to modify the adverb *faster* or the verb *was disappointed.*

**116. The verbs** *be, seem, appear, become, remain,* **and others of similar meaning are usually followed by adjectives. These adjectives complete the meaning of the verb and modify the subject of the verb. They are called** *predicate adjectives.*

Example 1. The room seems *cold.*

Here the noun *room* is being modified, not the verb *seems*, and so the adjective *cold* is used.

Example 2. As long as he is not hungry, the baby will remain *quiet.*

Example 3. The grass turned *brown* during the long drought.

**116a. Adverbs are used with** *become, appear, seem,* **and the like when it is the verb and not its subject that is modified.**

Example 1.  Eugene *quickly* became the leader of the group.
Example 2.  A flag appeared *suddenly* in the window.

**117. Verbs denoting impressions of the senses, such as *taste*, *smell*, *look*, *feel*, and *sound*, are usually followed by predicate adjectives (116).  These adjectives complete the meaning of the verb, but they modify or describe the subject of the verb.**

Example 1.  Mrs. Lyons sounded *angry*.
Example 2.  The dessert looks *good*.
Example 3.  Donald feels *bad* about the accident.

The sentences do not tell the manner in which the sounding, looking, or feeling was done, but tell the condition or quality of the subjects of the verbs.  Therefore adjectives are used and not adverbs.

**117a. Adverbs are used with verbs like *taste*, *smell*, *look*, and *sound* when it is the verb and not its subject that is modified.**

Example 1.  The handkerchief smelled *strongly* of perfume.
Example 2.  Harold tasted the cake *eagerly*.
Example 3.  The cake tastes *delicious*.

In examples 1 and 2, the adverbs *strongly* and *eagerly* modify the verbs *smelled* and *tasted*.  In example 3 the adjective *delicious* modifies the noun *cake*.

## II. Use of Comparatives and Superlatives

**118. Do not use "more" with an adjective to which *er* has already been added, or "most" with an adjective to which *est* has already been added.  Such double comparatives and superlatives are incorrect.  Never use "more better" or "worser."**

Example 1.  Tom is *lazier* than his brother.
Do not say "more lazier."  *Lazier* is already comparative.
Example 2.  Betty's cold is *worse* today.
*Worse* is the comparative form, and should never have an *r* added.

**119. The comparative degree is used in comparing two persons or things; the superlative is used in comparing more than two persons or things.**

Example 1.  Edward was the *more successful* of the two sons.
Example 2.  Both girls have passed the tests.  Miss Brown is the *faster* but Miss Curtis is the *more accurate*.
Example 3.  Ferris is the *most valuable* man on the baseball team.

In examples 1 and 2 comparative forms are used because in each case two persons are being compared, while in example 3 the superlative is used because Ferris is compared with all the other members of the team.

**120. The word *other* should be used after *than* in comparing one person or thing with the rest of a group to which the person or thing belongs.**

Example. Phillips is a *better* worker *than* any *other* man in his shop.

It would be illogical to say "than any man in his shop," for "any man in his shop" includes Phillips himself, and he cannot be a better worker than himself.

Any other word or phrase which would convey the same meaning as *other* may be used in place of *other*. For example, we might say, "Phillips is a better worker than any of the rest of the men in his shop."

**121. Never use "all the farther" or "all the further" for *as far as*, or "all the longer" for *as long as*, or similar substitutions for *as—as*.**

Example 1. Dan walked *farther* than the rest of us.

Example 2. This is *as far as* I can go.

The word *farther* is used correctly in example 1. It would be wrong to use "all the farther" or "all the further" in example 2.

**122. Some adjectives and adverbs do not logically have comparative and superlative forms. They express qualities or states that exist completely or not at all and do not exist in varying degrees. Among these are *square, unique, dead, empty, equal,* and *round,* and corresponding adverbs.**

Example 1. Bob's box is *more nearly empty* than Frank's.

It would be inaccurate to use "emptier" in this sentence, for to do so would imply that Frank's box is empty and Bob's is "more empty." *Empty* means containing nothing and "emptier" would therefore mean "containing less than nothing," which is impossible.

Example 2. All the boys have watches, but John's is *unique*.

*Unique* means *the only one of its kind*. We might say *John's is the most unusual,* but not "John's is the most unique."

*Note*: In everyday speech and writing words that are logically incapable of comparison are nevertheless frequently used in comparative and superlative degrees. In careful writing, however, such use should be avoided.

**123. *Fewer* means smaller in number, and *less* means smaller in amount.**

Example 1. *Fewer* than ten members were present.

Example 2. We have *less* time than they.

# III. Use of the Articles *A, An,* and *The*

**124.** **The choice of which indefinite article (106, 106a) to use depends upon the word that immediately follows the article. Before words beginning with a vowel (*a, e, i, o, u*) or a silent *h,* use *an.* Use *a* before words beginning with all other letters (consonants), with *o* sounded like *w,* or with *u* or *eu* pronounced "you."**

Example 1. I bought *an* old bicycle from *a* neighbor.

Example 2. He has *a* hard job and he is making *an* honest effort to do it well.

Example 3. You have *an* unusual opportunity to obtain *a* useful second-hand car.

Example 4. The game will be *a* one-sided contest.

**125.** **When two or more nouns joined by *and* refer to different persons or things, the article should often be used before each noun to avoid misunderstanding.**

Example 1. *The* captain and *the* instructor recommended Jim.

If the second *the* were omitted, this sentence would imply that one person was both captain and instructor.

Example 2. We need *an* electrician and *a* radio operator.

**125a.** **Two nouns denoting articles commonly thought of together are generally used without repeating the article before the second noun. Such pairs of nouns include *cup and saucer, hat and coat, shoes and stockings.***

Example 1. She bought *the* hat and coat in Los Angeles.

Example 2. Please give me *a* cup and saucer.

**126.** **When two or more nouns joined by *and* refer to the same person or thing, use the article before the first noun only.**

Example 1. Dr. Bell employs *a* nurse and technician.

The same person is both nurse and technician.

Example 2. Miss Tracy met *the* artist and writer in Chicago.

One person is both artist and writer.

**127.** **When two or more adjectives refer to different things or persons, but only one singular noun is used, the article should be repeated before each adjective.**

Example 1. Carol has *an* older and *a* younger brother.

There are two brothers, one older and one younger than Carol.

Example 2. *The* blue, *the* brown, and *the* gray suit should be pressed.

Three different suits are referred to.

**127a.** When two or more adjectives modify a singular noun and refer to one person or thing, the article is used only before the first adjective.

Example 1. He is *a* brave and intelligent soldier.

Example 2. Mrs. Harper bought *a* brown and yellow scarf.

**128. When two singular nouns that are being compared refer to the same person or thing, use the article only before the first noun.**

Example 1. Mr. Smith is *a* better speaker than writer.

Example 2. Willis is *a* more experienced carpenter than gardener.

This sentence means that Willis has had more experience in carpentry than he has had in gardening.

**128a.** When two singular nouns that are being compared refer to different persons or things, use the article before each noun.

Example. Charles is *a* better golf instructor than *a* professional golfer.

This sentence means that Charles teaches better than someone else, a professional golfer, would teach.

**129. Do not use *a* or *an* after *sort of* or *kind of*.**

Example 1. They are having some sort of celebration.

Example 2. What kind of book do you want?

It would be incorrect to say "some sort of a celebration" or "what kind of a book."

## IV. Miscellaneous Adjective and Adverb Problems

**130. Do not use the plural demonstrative adjectives "these" and "those" with the singular nouns *kind* and *sort*. Use *this* and *that*.**

Example 1. George doesn't like *that* kind of olives.

Example 2. We ought to play *this* sort of games more often.

Example 3. I don't want any of *those* kinds of candy.

It would be wrong to use "those kind" in example 1 or "these sort" in example 2. *Those* is correct in example 3 because it modifies the plural *kinds*.

**131. Do not use the adverbs "here" and "there" just after the adjectives *this*, *that*, *these*, or *those*.**

Example 1. Does *this* sweater belong to you?

Example 2. Ben has put *those* books on the shelf.

It is incorrect to say "this here sweater" or "those there books."

**132. Never use "them" to modify a noun.** *Them* **is a pronoun and never an adjective.**

Example 1. *Those* letters should be mailed today.

Example 2. Who broke *those* glasses?

It would be wrong to use "them" in place of *those* in these sentences.

**133. The words** *no, not* **(***n't***),** *none, nothing, nobody, no one, neither, never,* **and** *nowhere* **are** *negatives.* **Do not use more than one of them to express a negative idea.**

Example 1. We *haven't any* gasoline.

Example 2. James *was never* in New York.

Example 3. There *isn't anybody* at home.

It would be incorrect to use "haven't no," "wasn't never," and "isn't nobody" in these sentences.

**133a.** The words *only, scarcely, hardly,* and *but* are sometimes used in a negative sense. When they are so used, do not use other negatives with them.

Example 1. The tired boy *could hardly* walk.

Example 2. There *was only* one man on duty.

"Couldn't hardly" would be incorrect in example 1; "wasn't only" would be incorrect in example 2.

**134. Avoid the use of "kind of" and "sort of" as adverbs modifying adjectives or adverbs. Use** *rather, somewhat,* **or** *a little* **instead.**

Example 1. The patient has been *somewhat* restless all day.

Example 2. Mr. Hill spoke *rather* sharply to the clerk.

Expressions like "kind of restless" and "sort of sharply," while often heard in everyday conversation, should not be used in more formal speech or in writing.

**135. Do not add** *s* **to** *anywhere, somewhere,* **or** *nowhere.*

Example 1. The Carters live *somewhere* near here.

Example 2. I haven't seen Helen *anywhere.*

**136. Do not confuse** *two, too,* **and** *to. Two* **is an adjective (8) indicating number;** *too* **is an adverb (9) meaning** *more than enough* **or** *also; to* **is a preposition (10). Be sure to spell each one correctly.**

Example 1. The *two* boys went *to* the game.

Example 2. Is it *too* late *to* see the last show?

Example 3. There is enough for you and for John *too.*

**137.** *Very* and *too* should not be used alone to modify a past participle (19). *Much* or *greatly* or some other adverb should follow *very* or *too* in such cases.

Example 1. Hardy was *very much* annoyed at the delay.

Example 2. Gary was *too greatly* surprised to be able to protest.

**138.** In general, avoid placing an adverb between the two parts of an infinitive (19a), unless clearness or accuracy is gained by doing so.

Example 1. Henry told us *to come* to the office *immediately*.

Example 2. Ask him *to explain clearly* what he means.

**139.** A modifier should be so placed in the sentence that there is no doubt as to which word it modifies. *Only, merely, especially, nearly, almost,* and *never* should usually be placed next to the words they modify.

Example 1. Fred *only* wanted to borrow a few dollars.

Example 2. Fred wanted to borrow *only* a few dollars.

The first sentence means that all Fred wanted was to borrow a few dollars; *only* modifies the verb *wanted*. The second sentence means that Fred wanted to borrow a few dollars and not a large amount; *only* modifies the adjective *few*.

## PREPOSITIONS

**140.** The preposition (10) *of* is unnecessary after the verbs *remember, recall,* and *recollect*. Do not use it after these verbs.

Example 1. Allen *remembers* having heard the story many years ago.

Example 2. Helen can't *recollect* meeting anyone on the road.

It would be incorrect to say "remembers of having heard" or "can't recollect of meeting" in these sentences.

**141.** The word *where* means *to what place* or *at what place*. Do not use an unnecessary "to" or "at" with *where*.

Example 1. Where is Robert going?

Example 2. I don't know where my gloves are.

It would be wrong to say "Where is Robert going to?" or "where my gloves are at."

**142.** The expressions "want in," "want out," and "want off" should be avoided.

Example 1. The boys want *to come in*.

Example 2. She wants *to get off* at the next stop.

**143. Do not use "for to" in place of *to* in infinitives (19a) after the verbs *want, like,* and *ask.***

Example 1. Mr. Wilson wants to see you.
Example 2. His mother would like him to do it.
Example 3. I asked him to let me go.
Do not say "wants for to see you," "would like for him to do it," or "asked him for to let me go."

**144. Do not use "off" when you mean *from.***

Example 1. We buy our vegetables *from* Mr. Lucas.
Example 2. Don't take any money *from* Ted.
Example 3. Paul borrowed that tie *from* Bill.
It would be wrong to use "off" in place of *from* in any of these sentences.

**145. Do not use "of" after *off.* "Off of" is incorrect.**

Example 1. Playgrounds keep children *off* the streets.
Example 2. Mary's coat fell *off* the rack.

**146. Do not insert "of" between *had* and a past participle (19). (See also 54.)**

Example. If you *had asked* him, he would have told you.
It would be wrong to say "if you had of asked."

**147. Use *at home,* not "to home."**

Example 1. Is your brother *at home*?
Example 2. Anne will be *at home* all evening.

**148. Avoid the use of unnecessary prepositions, such as "up" after *divide, rest,* and *finish,* and "in" after *start.***

Example 1. They *divided* the profits among themselves.
Example 2. If we hurry we can *finish* by ten o'clock.
Example 3. You had better *start* to write your letter.
The expressions "divided up," "finish up," and "start in" should not be used in writing or in formal speech.

**149. Use the preposition *on* with the date or day of an occurrence unless it is preceded by *next* or *last.***

Example 1. The bill is due *on* the tenth of November.
Example 2. I saw him *on* Monday.
The *on* is not needed when we say, "It happened last November" or "I shall see him next Wednesday."

**150. Use the preposition *behind* rather than "in back of."**

Example. What is *behind* that screen?

**151. In formal speech and in writing, use** *in that way* **and** *in this way* **to tell** *how*, **rather than "that way" and "this way."**

Example 1. We cannot be successful if we continue to operate *in this way*.

Example 2. There are good reasons for settling the matter *in that way*.

**152. Do not omit** *of* **before** *no use* **or** *little use* **following** *is*, *was*, **or some other form of the verb** *to be*, **except when the verb is preceded by** *there*.

Example 1. The car is *of* no use without tires.

"The car is no use" would be incorrect.

Example 2. His early training will be *of* no use in this work.

Example 3. There is no use in telling him.

This sentence is correct.

**153.** *Between* **is used in speaking of two persons or things, or in speaking of two groups.** *Among* **is used in speaking of more than two.**

Example 1. Divide the pie *between* Jack and Sally.

Example 2. The estate was divided *among* the five heirs.

*Note:* In some cases *between* is used in speaking of more than two, when *among* would be awkward. For example, we might say, "An agreement was made between England, Russia, and the United States." In this case the agreement is made between each one of the countries and each of the others.

**154. Use** *into*, **not "in," to introduce a prepositional phrase (10) that implies** *entrance into* **something rather than existence or action within it.**

Example 1. Carl ran *into* the yard.

Example 2. The baby was playing *in* the yard.

Example 3. Take Mr. Wells *into* the office.

**155.** *Besides* **means** *in addition to*; *beside* **means** *by the side of*. **Do not use "beside" when you mean** *besides*.

Example 1. Mrs. Ennis stood *beside* her husband.

Example 2. He has two brothers in high school *besides* the one in college.

**156. Do not use "inside of" for** *within* **in an expression of time.**

Example 1. He will telephone *within* an hour.

Example 2. We can finish the job *within* three weeks.

**157.** *Different* **and** *differently* **should be followed by** *from* **rather than by "to" or "than."**

Example 1. His fountain pen is different *from* that.

Example 2. They dress differently *from* us.

**158. When the verb *follow* is used in the passive voice (17b), a prepositional phrase (10) telling what or who did the following should begin with *by*, not "with."**

Example 1. The team's early victories were followed *by* a series of defeats.

Example 2. The speeches will be followed *by* a discussion period.

**159. Use *angry with* when referring to a person. Use *angry at* when referring to a thing.**

Example 1. Sam was very angry *with* the other boys.

Example 2. Mrs. Smith is angry *at* the delay in filling her order.

**160. Use *accompanied by* when referring to persons and animals. Use *accompanied with* when referring to things.**

Example 1. Miss Norris was accompanied *by* her brother.

Example 2. The illness is accompanied *with* a high fever.

**161. Use *differ with* to express disagreement of opinion. Use *differ from* to express unlikeness between persons or things.**

Example 1. Gerald *differs with* me on that question.
Gerald's opinion is not the same as mine.

Example 2. The new airplane *differs from* the old model in many ways.
There are many ways in which the new airplane is not like the old model.

**162. Do not use "die with" to express cause of death. *Die of* is correct.**

Example. Her father *died of* tuberculosis.

## CONJUNCTIONS

**163. A conjunction (12) that connects a subordinate clause (2) to the principal clause is a *subordinating conjunction*. Among the subordinating conjunctions are *after*, *as*, *because*, *if*, *that*, *unless*, *when*, *whether*, and *although*.**

Example. Fred went home *after* he had closed the store.

**164. A conjunction that connects two words, two phrases (10), two subordinate clauses (2), or two principal clauses (2) is a *co-ordinating conjunction*. *And*, *or*, and *but* are co-ordinating conjunctions.**

Example 1. Jane speaks *and* reads French very well.

Example 2. You will find the stamps on the table *or* in the desk drawer.

Example 3. Harvey went to college not because he wanted to go, *but* because his father wished him to be an engineer.

**164a.** When two principal clauses (2) are joined by a coordinating conjunction (164), the resulting sentence is a *compound sentence* (223).

Example. Stephen is in the Army *and* his brother is in the Navy.

**164b.** The conjunction *but* is used to join clauses that express contrasting or opposing ideas.

Example 1. The fireman tried to revive the girl, *but* it was too late.
Example 2. Charles was hungry, *but* he would not touch the food.

**165. Do not use "like" in place of *as* or *as if* or *as though* to introduce a subordinate clause.**

Example 1. The boys did their work *as* they were told.
Example 2. Martha doesn't feel *as though* she ought to go.

**166. Do not use the prepositions "without" or "except" in place of the conjunction *unless* to introduce a subordinate clause.**

Example 1. He will not go *unless* you can go with him.
Example 2. *Unless* his leave is canceled, Irwin will be here next week.
It would be wrong to say "without you can go with him" or "except his leave is canceled."

**167. When the preposition *except* introduces a subordinate clause, the preposition is followed by *that*.**

Example. The house suits us, *except that* the bedrooms are too small.

**168. Use *that* (or *whether*), not "as," to introduce a subordinate clause (2) following the verbs *think, say, believe, know,* and others of similar meaning.**

Example 1. Everyone thought *that* he was telling the truth.
Example 2. I don't know *whether* there is time to finish the job tonight.

**169. Do not use "where" in place of *that*.**

Example 1. I see *that* we are going to have a new supervisor.
Example 2. John read in the paper *that* men are needed at the plant.
To use "where" instead of *that* in these sentences would be incorrect.

**170. Do not use "on account of" to introduce a clause; use *because*.**

Example. Bob can't go *because* he has a cold.
It would be wrong to say "on account of he has a cold."

**171. After *neither* use *nor*, not "or."**

Example 1. *Neither* Mr. Wyman *nor* Mr. Shaw will be in today.
Example 2. Crawford's plan will *neither* reduce our expenses *nor* increase our output.

**171a. After *either* use *or*, not "nor."**

Example. Mrs. Ramsey did not invite *either* Elsie *or* Constance.

**172. Do not omit the second *as* in comparing two persons o. things.**

Example 1.  You have done *as* much *as* Lewis, if not more.
It is incorrect to say "You have done as much if not more than Lewis."
Example 2.  This road is *as* bad *as* the other one, or worse.
"This road is as bad or worse than the other one" would be incorrect.

**173. Use the conjunction *that*, not "because," to introduce a noun clause (225) that is the subject of the sentence.**

Example. *That* David failed in his first attempt doesn't prove that he will never succeed.

*That David failed in his first attempt* is the subject of the sentence.  It would be wrong to begin this clause with "because."

**173a. Avoid the use of "because" to introduce a noun clause following *the reason is* or *the reason was*. Use *that* to introduce such a clause.**

Example. The reason for the delay is *that* we cannot get the needed materials.

While we often hear in everyday conversation such expressions as "The reason I came is because you sent for me," this use of "because" should be avoided in more careful speech and in writing.

**174. Avoid the use of "if" for *whether* to introduce a clause serving as the object (17a, 225) of *tell*, *ask*, *say*, *know*, or a verb of similar meaning, especially if the words *or not* are used.**

Example 1.  Peter didn't tell me *whether* he would come or not.
Example 2.  No one knows *whether* the meeting will be held next week.

**175. Use *so that* rather than "so" alone, to introduce a clause indicating purpose.**

Example. We are sending an itemized bill *so that* you can see just what purchases were made.

**176. Avoid the use of "than" and "until" for *when*. A comparative expression is followed by *than*.**

Example 1.  We had hardly started to eat *when* the visitors arrived.
Example 2.  He hadn't driven two miles *when* the car broke down.
It would be incorrect to use "than" in example 1 or "until" in example 2.
Example 3.  He had no sooner stopped than a tire blew out.
*Than* is correctly used in example 3.

# CAPITALIZATION

**177. The first word in every sentence begins with a capital letter.**

Example. In a few minutes we reached the station. None of us knew just when the train was due.

**178. The names of particular persons, places, or things are called *proper nouns*. All proper nouns should begin with capital letters.**

Example 1. The new foreman is Robert Johnson.

Example 2. The largest city in the United States is New York.

Example 3. The Senate and the House of Representatives meet in the Capitol.

**178a. Words used to name a particular brand or product are capitalized.**

Example 1. Mr. Wilkins has driven a Chevrolet for years.

Example 2. Can you fill an order for one gross of Mazda lamps?

**179. In the names of organizations and associations, such as political, religious, social, scientific, and commercial ones, begin each word with a capital letter except prepositions, articles, and conjunctions.**

Example 1. He is the recognized leader of the Republican Party.

Example 2. Mr. Weaver is a member of the Presbyterian Church.

Example 3. Mrs. Bates belongs to the Daughters of the American Revolution.

**180. Adjectives derived from proper nouns begin with capital letters, unless the original meaning is remote and the adjective has become a common one.**

Example 1. The Democratic candidate for mayor is of Irish ancestry.

Example 2. Our family prefers pasteurized milk.

**181. Nouns indicating nationality or membership in a particular organization begin with capital letters.**

Example 1. On the board of directors there are Catholics, Protestants, and Jews.

Example 2. The American explained the game of baseball to the Englishman and the Brazilian.

**181a. The names of languages begin with capital letters.**

Example. Mary is studying French this year.

**182. Initials standing for the names of persons or organizations, or for the professional rank of a person, are written with capital letters.**

Example 1. The letter is addressed to J. M. Conway.

Example 2. The union is affiliated with the A. F. of L.

**183. Every line of poetry should begin with a capital letter.**

Example. Listen, my children, and you shall hear
Of the midnight ride of Paul Revere.

**184. The first word of a sentence that is directly quoted should begin with a capital letter.**

Example. George said, "The best thing you can do is to get some rest."

**184a.** When a direct quotation is broken by words such as *he said*, the second part of the quotation does not begin with a capital letter unless it is a new sentence.

Example 1. "I believe," said Miss Hays, "that you are wrong about that."

Example 2. "I see what you mean," admitted Bob. "Let's try it another way."

**185. Names of the days of the week, of holidays, and of months of the year begin with capital letters.**

Example 1. We vote for President on the first Tuesday after the first Monday in November.

Example 2. We celebrate Washington's Birthday on February 22.

**186. The names of the seasons of the year should not be capitalized except when they are personified, as sometimes in poetry.**

Example 1. He went to Camp Wheeler in the summer and remained until late fall.

Example 2. We felt Winter's icy breath on our cheeks.

**187. The words *north*, *south*, *east*, and *west*, and combinations or derivatives of these words, are capitalized when they refer to regions of the country. When they indicate direction, they are not capitalized.**

Example 1. Helen had always lived in the South.

Example 2. The birds will soon be flying north again.

Example 3. Two of the boys are from Western states.

**188. All the important words in the titles of books, magazines, poems, other literary compositions, works of art, plays, motion pictures, and musical compositions are capitalized. Prepositions, articles, and conjunctions are not capitalized unless one of them is the first or the last word in the title.**

Example 1. The boys have been reading *The Last of the Mohicans* and *In Darkest Africa*.

Example 2.  Carol likes the poem, "Stopping by Woods on a Snowy Evening."

**189. Titles indicating office, rank, or relationship are capitalized when used with proper names.**

Example 1.  He has often spoken of Uncle William.

Example 2.  Among the guests were Governor Thompson, Captain Phillips, and Doctor Jones.

**189a. When titles indicating office, rank, or relationship are used without the names and do not identify particular individuals, they are not capitalized.**

Example 1.  He told me that he had an aunt in Boston.

Example 2.  One of her brothers is a doctor and the other is a lieutenant in the Army.

**189b. Titles and names of offices that identify particular persons are capitalized.**

Example.  The Secretary of State and the Mexican Ambassador conferred with the President.

**190. Capitalize common nouns, such as *street*, *park*, *school*, *river*, *hospital*, *railroad*, and *club*, when they are used as part of a proper name.**

Example 1.  The park extends from Franklin Street to Walnut Avenue.

Example 2.  Blandfield Hospital is not far from Madison Park.

Example 3.  Richard has never seen either the Rocky Mountains or the Mississippi River.

**191. The names of important historical events and documents are capitalized.**

Example 1.  The Battle of Gettysburg marked the turning point of the Civil War.

Example 2.  In Washington you may see the Declaration of Independence.

**192. Nouns (and usually pronouns) referring to God and Christ are capitalized.**

Example 1.  Serve the Lord with gladness; come before His presence with singing.

Example 2.  The Son of Man shall come in the glory of His Father with His angels.

**193. Names for the Bible, or parts of it, are capitalized.**

Example 1.  He opened the Bible at the page where the New Testament began.

Example 2. Mrs. Burch could always quote an apt verse from the Scriptures.

**194. The word *I* is always written as a capital letter.**

Example. I said that I would go with him.

# PUNCTUATION

The period, question mark, comma, semicolon, colon, exclamation mark, and quotation mark are marks of *punctuation.* Punctuation marks help the reader to understand written matter. The omission or misplacing of a single mark of punctuation may change the meaning of what you write.

**195. Use a period at the end of a declarative or an imperative sentence.    (See 3, 4.)    Do not insert a period before the end of a sentence is reached.**

Example 1. Although he knew the dangers that he might encounter, Bruce was determined to carry out his plan.

It would be incorrect to use a period instead of the comma after *encounter.* The clause beginning with *Although* is not a sentence but a subordinate clause forming part of the complete sentence.

Example 2. We are sending you a copy of a letter that we received from our Chicago office.

It would be wrong to put a period after *letter* and begin a new sentence with *that. That we received from the Chicago office* is a subordinate clause (2) modifying *letter* and must not be written as a separate sentence.

**196. Use a period after every abbreviation, including initials and abbreviated titles preceding names.**

Examples.    Mr. G. E. Coleman, Jr.        815 Broad St.
             Col. Holmes      Dr. J. E. Edwards        Mrs. Grayson
             U. S.        Ariz.        Ill.        sq. ft.        doz.        qt.

*Note:* The initials of some United States Government agencies are often written without periods and without spacing between letters, as in the following examples:

FBI        OPA        WLB        FHA

**196a. Never write an abbreviated title, such as *Dr.,* unless the name follows it.**

Example. We sent for Dr. John Edwards.
Do not write "We sent for the dr. yesterday."

**196b. Do not use "Rev." with a last name alone. This abbreviation should be used only when a first name or an initial is also used.**

Example. Rev. Edward J. Smith

Never write "Rev. Smith."

**197. Use a question mark at the end of an interrogative sentence (3, 4). Do not use a question mark at the end of a declarative or an imperative sentence containing an indirect question.**

Example 1. What is the reason for her absence?

Example 2. He asked what was the reason for her absence.

Example 3. Tell me what is the reason for her absence.

Example 1 is a direct question, or interrogative sentence, and requires a question mark. Examples 2 and 3 contain indirect questions. They are not interrogative sentences. Example 2 is a declarative and example 3 is an imperative sentence. Neither should end with a question mark.

**198. The exclamation point is used after sentences beginning with the exclamatory *how* or *what*, and after other sentences that indicate surprise, anger, or other strong emotion.**

Example 1. How tall you have grown!

Example 2. What a good time we had!

Example 3. At last you have come!

**198a. The exclamation point is used after words or phrases that have no grammatical function in a sentence but indicate strong emotion. Such expressions are called *interjections*.**

Example 1. Oh! I didn't know there was anyone here.

Example 2. Great Scott! Is it as late as that?

**199. When the clauses of a compound sentence (164a) are joined by a conjunction, a comma is usually required before the conjunction.**

Example 1. There will be a business and social meeting on October 28 at the clubhouse, and every member is urged to bring a friend.

Example 2. Everyone tried to persuade Mr. Taylor to stay, but nothing could make him change his mind.

*Note*: When the clauses of a compound sentence are short, it is not necessary to use a comma.

Example. The door was locked and the lights were out.

**200. Commas are used to separate words, phrases, or clauses used in series in a sentence.**

Example 1. She has had experience in selling shoes, hats, and jewelry in our store.

Example 2. Policemen are stationed outside the gates, at the door, and inside the building.

Example 3. Joan prepared the sandwiches, Mary baked a cake, and Edith made candy.

*Note*: When there is a conjunction between each two items in the series, commas are not needed.

Example. Albert or James or Tom will help you.

**201. When a series of three or more adjectives is used before a noun, separate the adjectives by commas. In a series of two adjectives omit the comma if the first adjective modifies the combination of the second adjective and the noun.**

Example 1. This is an accurate, sturdy, dependable watch.

Example 2. She has a tall, handsome, young brother.

Example 3. This is an accurate, dependable watch.

Example 4. She has a handsome young brother.

**202. A nonrestrictive clause (226a) should be separated from the rest of the sentence by a comma or commas. Do not use commas with a restrictive clause (226).**

Example 1. They asked Mr. Gibson, who knew French very well, to translate the letter.

Example 2. The company needs a man who can handle personnel problems.

Example 3. I can let you use my typewriter, which is in fairly good condition.

Example 4. Please send us any information that you have on this subject.

In example 1, the clause *who knew French very well* could be omitted without changing the meaning of the sentence. It is a nonrestrictive clause and is therefore set off by commas. The clause in example 3 is likewise nonrestrictive, and is separated by a comma from the rest of the sentence. In examples 2 and 4, the clauses *who can handle personnel problems* and *that you have on this subject* are restrictive. To omit them would change the meaning of the sentences. Therefore they are not set off by commas.

**203. When an adverbial clause (225) comes at the beginning of a sentence, it is set off from the rest of the sentence by a comma.**

Example 1. When he heard the alarm, Howard went immediately to his post.

Example 2. If you are not willing to go, we can send Miss Masson.

**204. An appositive (70), together with any words or phrases used with it as modifiers, is set off by commas.**

Example 1. The treasurer, Mr. Weaver, has been with the company for many years.

Example 2. They have recommended Mrs. Armstrong, the woman I told you about.

*Note:* Sometimes when the connection between the words in apposition is very close and the appositive is a single word, commas are not used.

Example 1. We boys have applied for jobs in the plant.

Example 2. Her son David is at school in Virginia.

**205. Words, phrases, or clauses that are inserted as side remarks or comments into sentences grammatically complete without them are called *parenthetical expressions.* Such expressions are separated from the rest of the sentence by commas.**

Example 1. Your suggestion, we are glad to say, has already been adopted.

Example 2. Mr. Carlin's invention is, he believes, of great importance in the industry.

**206. Use a comma to separate the name of a city from the name of a state or country following it. When the name of the state or country follows the name of the city within a sentence, put a comma after the name of the state or country also.**

Example 1. Houston, Texas, is one of the largest cities in the South.

Example 2. The firm has an office in Rio de Janeiro, Brazil.

**207. The items in a date are the day of the week (if it is given), the day of the month, and the year. These items should be separated by commas. When the date is written in a sentence, a comma should also be placed after the last item, unless it ends the sentence.**

Example 1. On Monday, October 26, 1942, he began his new duties.

Example 2. The letter was written on November 3, 1941.

Example 3. On Thursday, May 10, I shall be in New York.

**208. Do not put a comma between the subject of a sentence and the verb, unless, of course, the verb is preceded by an appositive (70, 204), a nonrestrictive clause (202, 226a), a parenthetical expression (205), or some other element requiring commas.**

Example 1. All the articles on your list can be supplied immediately.

Example 2. Everyone who registered last month may vote in the election.

It would be incorrect to place a comma after *list* in example 1 or *month* in example 2.

**209. Do not put a comma between a verb and its object or a predicate nominative (71), unless there is a parenthetical expression (205) between them requiring commas.**

Example 1. The laboratory experiments proved that the new chemical was effective.

In this sentence the clause *that the new chemical was effective* is the object of the verb *proved*. It would be incorrect to insert a comma after *proved*.

Example 2. The secret of Harry's popularity is his cheerful disposition.

It would be wrong to insert a comma between the verb *is* and the predicate nominative *his cheerful disposition*.

**210. Use a comma after *yes, no,* or *well* occurring at the beginning of a sentence.**

Example 1. Yes, this is my hat.
Example 2. No, Alfred isn't here.
Example 3. Well, what can we do?

**211. The name of the person addressed, or a title or other term applied to him, is set off by a comma or commas when written in a sentence.**

Example 1. What is your opinion, Everett?
Example 2. Mrs. Nelson, there was a telephone call for you.
Example 3. I hope, my boy, that you will profit by your experience.

**212. Two or more independent sentences closely connected in thought may sometimes be written as a compound sentence (164a, 223) without a conjunction to join them. When this is done, use a semicolon between the independent clauses.**

Example 1. I do not believe he is guilty; no one who knows him could believe it.

Example 2. These instructions must be followed exactly; otherwise our plan will fail.

**213. A colon is used before a series of items introduced by the words *the following* or *as follows,* either expressed or implied.**

Example. The officials to be chosen in this election are as follows: governor, representative in Congress, delegate to the legislature, five county commissioners.

**214. When the exact words of a speaker or writer are quoted, they should be enclosed in quotation marks. Words introducing the quotation are separated from the quotation by a comma.**

Example. Frank said, "We can start whenever you are ready."

**215. Do not use quotation marks for an indirect quotation; use them only when the exact words of the person quoted are repeated.**

Example 1. The captain said that his men could be relied upon.

It would be incorrect to put *his men could be relied upon* in quotation marks.

Example 2. Bob asked who had brought the books.

It would be incorrect to use quotation marks in this sentence.

**216. When a direct quotation is broken by an expression such as *he said*, each part of the quotation should be enclosed in quotation marks.**

Example. "Benson could do it," said Mr. Simpson, "but I don't think he will."

**217. Use single quotation marks around quoted material that is included within another quotation.**

Example. "Then he said, 'I don't believe a word of it,' and walked away," explained the girl.

**218. When a direct quotation is followed by an expression like *he said*, a comma is placed after the quoted words, unless the quotation is a question or an exclamation. Never use a period or a semicolon after a quotation followed by *he said* or a similar expression.**

Example 1. "We have plenty of time," he said.
Example 2. "Look out!" exclaimed Ralph.
Example 3. "Where is that file?" asked Miss Hammond.

**219. When a quotation is broken by words such as *he said*, a period should be placed after these words if the second part of the quotation is a new sentence. If the second part of the quotation continues a sentence begun in the first, put a comma after the words that break the quotation.**

Example 1. "I don't like this game," Arthur said. "There isn't enough action in it."

Example 2. "I think," said Mr. Ames with a smile, "that you have done enough work for one day."

**220. When a final quotation mark occurs with a period or a comma, place the period or comma inside the quotation mark. When a final quotation mark occurs with a question mark or an exclamation point, the question mark or exclamation point is placed inside the quotation mark if it belongs with the quoted matter; otherwise it is placed outside.**

Example 1.  Betty said, "I'm glad you came."
Example 2.  Carl asked, "When is Alice coming?"
Example 3.  Who said, "Give me liberty or give me death"?

**221. When the title of a book, magazine, work of art, or musical composition appears in a printed sentence, it is printed in *italics*. In handwriting or typewriting, it is underlined. The title of a chapter, poem, essay, or magazine article is enclosed in quotation marks.**

Example 1.  You will find "The Rime of the Ancient Mariner" in *The Oxford Book of English Verse*.

Example 2.  I have the two-volume edition of America in Midpassage by Charles and Mary Beard.

# SENTENCE STRUCTURE

The way in which words are put together to form sentences (rules 1 to 4, pages 108, 109) is called *sentence structure*. The clearness and effectiveness of our speech and writing depend upon our skill in constructing sentences. In order to express meaning clearly and exactly it is necessary to know something of the principles upon which sentences are constructed.

Sentences are classified according to meaning as declarative, imperative, or interrogative (3). They are also classified according to structure as *simple, compound,* or *complex*.

**222. A sentence that contains one subject and one predicate is a *simple sentence*.**

Example.  The tall young man walked quickly into the room.

The subject of this sentence is *the tall young man* and the predicate is *walked quickly into the room*.

**222a. Either the subject or the predicate of a simple sentence, or both, may have two or more parts of equal value. In such a case, the sentence has a compound subject, or a compound predicate, or both.**

Example 1.  John and Bill are going with us.
Example 2.  The men quickly loaded their guns and fired.

In example 1 the subject of the sentence, *John and Bill*, contains two nouns of equal importance. It is a compound subject.

In example 2 there are two predicate verbs (7), *loaded* and *fired*. Thus the sentence has a compound predicate. Both sentences are simple sentences.

**223.** Two or more groups of words, each of which could stand alone as an independent sentence, may be joined by a comma and a conjunction and written as one sentence, if there is a logical connection in thought between them.    Such a sentence is a *compound sentence*, and the two or more parts are called coordinate clauses.    Sometimes a semicolon instead of a comma and a conjunction is used between the clauses of a compound sentence (212).

Example 1.    Mr. Willard dictated the letter, but it has not been mailed.

Example 2.    The lights were dimmed; the curtain was raised; the play began.

**224.** A sentence having a main clause and one or more subordinate clauses (2) is a *complex sentence.*

Example.    Mrs. Clay has paid for the goods that she ordered last week.

The subordinate clause in this sentence is *that she ordered last week.* The rest of the sentence is the main clause.

**225.** Subordinate clauses serve as nouns, as adjectives, or as adverbs.    A *noun clause* may be the subject (1) or object (17a) of a verb, a predicate nominative (71), or the object of a preposition (10).    An *adjective clause* modifies a noun or pronoun. An *adverbial clause* modifies a verb, an adjective, or an adverb. (See also 11.)

Example 1.    Whatever you do will be satisfactory to us.

Example 2.    James said that the plans would be finished tomorrow.

In example 1 the noun clause *whatever you do* is the subject of the sentence.    In example 2 the noun clause *that the plans would be finished tomorrow* is the object of the verb *said.*

Example 3.    Give this invoice to Mr. Walsh, who sits at that desk near the window.

The adjective clause *who sits at that desk near the window* modifies the noun *Mr. Walsh.*

Example 4.    If I had known the facts, I could have explained the matter to Stanley when he was here.

This sentence contains two adverbial clauses modifying the verb *could have explained.*    The first, *if I had known the facts*, denotes condition, and the second, *when he was here*, denotes time.

**226.** An adjective clause is a *restrictive clause* if it limits or defines the word it modifies in such a way that omission of the clause would change the meaning of the sentence.    The relative pronoun introducing the clause is often omitted.    (See also 202.)

Example 1. The inspectors discarded all the tubes that were defective.
Example 2. All the tubes the inspectors discarded were defective.
The pronoun *which* (or *that*) following *tubes* is understood.

**226a. An adjective clause that merely gives some additional information about the word it modifies, and which could be omitted without materially changing the meaning of the sentence, is a *nonrestrictive clause*. (See also 202.)**

Example. Your new assistant will be Dan Ferguson, who is an excellent draftsman.

**227. A group of words having a single grammatical function in a sentence but not having a subject and a predicate is a *phrase*. Some phrases are introduced by prepositions (10, 10a) and some by participles (19).**

Example 1. The girl behind the counter nodded in agreement.

There are two prepositional phrases in this sentence, *behind the counter* and *in agreement*. The first modifies the noun *girl* and the second modifies the verb *nodded*.

Example 2. The man driving the car did not see the child.
*Driving the car* is a participial phrase modifying the noun *man*.

**228. Do not write a part of a sentence as though it were a complete sentence. (See also 195.)**

Example 1. The boy running down the street is Tom Clark.

It would be incorrect to write "The boy running down the street" as though it were a complete sentence. The word *running* is here a participial adjective modifying *boy*, and cannot stand as a verb without an auxiliary such as *is* or *was*. *The boy was running down the street* would be a complete sentence.

Example 2. Bernard ran into the blazing warehouse before anyone could stop him.

It would be incorrect to put a period after *warehouse* and begin *before* with a capital letter. *Before anyone could stop him* is a subordinate clause and should not be written as though it were a sentence.

Example 3. Mr. Hanley has had good training for this position, having worked for a number of years in the coal business.

It would be wrong to write "having worked for a number of years in the coal business" as if it were a separate sentence, for this is a participial phrase modifying *Mr. Hanley*.

Example 4. John insisted on doing all the work himself without help from anyone.

*Without help from anyone* is a prepositional phrase. To write it as a sentence would be incorrect.

**229. Do not run two independent (principal or main) clauses together as a compound sentence (223) without using a comma and a conjunction, or a semicolon, between them. A comma alone is not sufficient to join them.**

Example 1. It was an interesting play, and I enjoyed it very much.

It would be incorrect to write, "It was an interesting play I enjoyed it very much." It would also be incorrect to write, "It was an interesting play, I enjoyed it very much."

Example 2. Let Paul make the sketches; he can draw well.

*Note:* When there is a series of three or more short independent clauses in a sentence, a comma alone may be used between all but the last two, where both the conjunction and the comma are ordinarily used.

Example. The wind blew fiercely, lightning flashed, thunder roared, and the rain came down in sheets.

**230. Do not combine in a compound sentence two or more ideas that have no close relation to each other.**

Example. Dorothy Carter will be here next week. She is one of my best friends.

It would be incorrect to say, "Dorothy Carter will be here next week and she is one of my best friends," because there is no obvious relation between the two statements.

**231. Do not run too many independent clauses together, using *and, so,* or *but* to join them. Make separate sentences if necessary, or use subordinate clauses to make clear the relations between the ideas.**

Example 1. When we turned your order over to Mr. Harrison, who usually handles these matters, he was busy and gave it to a new clerk. The mistake was made because the new clerk did not understand the order.

The meaning of these sentences is clear. It would be awkward and less clear to put these ideas into such a rambling compound sentence as the following: "We turned your order over to Mr. Harrison, who usually handles these matters, and he was busy and he gave it to a new clerk and the new clerk did not understand it so the mistake was made."

**232. Do not use several short separate sentences to express related ideas that can be expressed better in one sentence using subordinating or co-ordinating expressions.**

Example. As soon as Mr. Goodwin came in, everyone began to ask questions, but he refused to answer.

This sentence is smoother and clearer than the following: "Mr. Goodwin came in. Everyone began to ask questions. He refused to answer."

### 233. Every modifier (8 to 11) should be so placed that there is no doubt as to which word it modifies.

Example 1. The materials will be sent by parcel post as soon as we receive your check.

The phrase *by parcel post*, which modifies the verb *will be sent*, is correctly placed in this example. It would be confusing to write, "The materials will be sent as soon as we receive your check by parcel post."

Example 2. I have just ordered for my car a radio with pushbutton controls.

The meaning of this sentence is clear, but it would not be clear if the sentence read "I have just ordered a radio for my car with pushbutton controls."

### 233a. Usually a relative clause should immediately follow the antecedent of the relative pronoun that introduces the clause.

Example. We received from the company a letter which explained the delay.

The sentence as shown in the example is preferable to "We received a letter from the company which explained the delay."

### 234. In using participles (19) and participial phrases (227), be sure that the word to be modified is expressed and that the references are clear.

Example 1. Walking along the road, John thought the moon looked unusually large.

It would be incorrect to say, "Walking along the road, the moon looked unusually large to John."

Example 2. Finding no one at home, the postman left a note in the mail slot.

It would be incorrect to say, "Finding no one at home, a note was left in the mail slot."

### 235. The antecedent (76) to which a pronoun refers should be clear. Do not use a pronoun for which there is no antecedent. Do not use the same pronoun twice in the same sentence to refer to different persons or things if the reference would not be clear.

Example 1. The cake should be cold before the icing is put on it.

In this sentence it is clear that the antecedent of *it* is *cake*. But if the sentence read, "The icing should not be put on the cake until it is cold," we could not be sure whether *it* referred to *cake* or *icing*.

Example 2. Bob is a poor speaker but he has been practicing to improve his speaking.

If this sentence read, "Bob is a poor speaker but he has been practicing to improve it," there would be no antecedent for "it."

Example 3. Jim told Philip's brother that he had recommended Philip for the job.

The meaning of this sentence would not be clear if it read, "Jim told Philip's brother that he had recommended him for the job."

## 236. Do not omit the subject and verb of a subordinate clause (2) when the subject is different from the subject of the main clause.

Example 1. While I was waiting on the corner, three busses passed me without stopping.

Example 2. When frightened, the bird gives a loud cry.

In example 2, it is permissible to omit the subject and verb of the clause. *Bird,* the subject of the main clause, is also the subject of the subordinate clause. In example 1, however, it would be incorrect to omit *I was,* for to do so would make the sentence mean that the busses were waiting on the corner.

## 237. A clause should not modify a word in the possessive case. Either the word should be put in the nominative or the objective case, or the clause should be made to modify a word following the possessive.

Example 1. I like the technique of Nash, who painted the murals in the lobby.

Example 2. I like Nash's technique, which is demonstrated in his murals in the lobby.

Example 3. Nash, who painted the murals in the lobby, has a technique that impresses me greatly.

In examples 1 and 3 *who painted the murals in the lobby* modifies *Nash*. In example 2 the relative clause modifies *technique*. It would be incorrect to say, "I admire Nash's technique, who painted the murals in the lobby," as this would make the relative clause modify the possessive *Nash's*.

*Note*: The following is an example of a seeming exception: *I bought this hat at Morton's, where I have a charge account.* In this case, however, *Morton's* is merely a shortened form of *Morton's Store* and is in the objective case.

**238. When two noun clauses are the object of a verb, do not omit the conjunction or relative pronoun introducing the second clause if there is a possibility of doubt as to the meaning.**

Example. Fred believes *that* you can do the work and *that* Mr. Miller will give you the job.

If the second *that* were omitted, the words "Mr. Miller will give you the job" might be read as a separate independent clause rather than as the object of "believes."

**238a. When two subordinate clauses modify the same noun or verb, the conjunction should be used in both clauses if necessary for clearness.**

Example. Dora returned to the town *where* she had grown up and *where* her brother still lived.

**239. When *which* is the object of the verb in the clause it introduces, do not use another object in the clause, such as "it" or "them." (See also 94.)**

Example. He told me a long story, which I didn't believe.
It would be incorrect to add "it" after *believe* in this sentence.

**240. Do not omit *that* in a clause beginning with an infinitive (19a) when the clause follows a verb such as *say, know, think,* or *feel.***

Example 1. He says *that* to finish the job tomorrow is impossible.
Example 2. Ellis knows *that* to win he must use all his skill.

**241. Do not use "when" or "where" clauses as predicate nominatives (71) in definitions or explanations.**

Example 1. Artificial respiration is the forcing of air into and out of an unconscious person's lungs.

It would be incorrect to say, "Artificial respiration is when you force air into and out of an unconscious person's lungs."

Example 2. To be in a quandary is to be uncertain what to do.
It would be incorrect to say, "To be in a quandary is where someone is uncertain what to do."

**242. When two modifiers of the same form apply to the same word in a sentence, it is usually better to place them together than to separate them.**

Example. After he had finished his work and had locked up the building, Carson went home.

It would be awkward to say, "After he had finished his work, Carson went home after he had locked up the building." It is better to combine the two clauses as in the example.

**243. Do not place between two parts of a sentence a modifier that might apply to either part.**

Example 1.  Before he left, Bill told Elsie he would write to her.

Example 2.  Bill told Elsie he would write to her before he left.

It is clear that in example 1 *before he left* modifies *told* and that in example 2 *before he left* modifies *write.*  If, however, we said, "Bill told Elsie before he left he would write to her," it would not be clear which word "before he left" was intended to modify.

**244. When two or more elements in a sentence are joined by co-ordinating conjunctions, they should be of parallel construction; for example, they may be all noun constructions or all verb constructions, but not a combination of the two.**

Example 1.  The school teaches shorthand, bookkeeping, and the use of business machines.

It would be incorrect to say, "The school teaches shorthand, bookkeeping, and to use business machines."

Example 2.  The nurse wrote down my name, my address, and my age.

It would be incorrect to use "how old I was" instead of *my age* in this sentence.

**245. When one series is used within another, the conjunction should not be omitted in the first series.**

Example.  In the morning the campers rose, washed, *and* dressed, and ate the chicken.

The meaning would not be clear if the sentence read "rose, washed, dressed, and ate the chicken."

**246. The correlative conjunctions *either—or*, *neither—nor*, *not only—but also*, *both—and*, and *whether—or* should usually be followed by sentence elements of similar construction.**

Example 1.  The boys have time neither for reading nor for going to the movies.

It would be incorrect to say "neither for reading nor to go to the movies."

Example 2.  This material can be used for either draperies or slip covers.

It would be incorrect to say, "This material either can be used for draperies or slip covers."  The *either* should be so placed that it is followed by the same construction as the *or*.

**247. Do not make inconsistent changes in person, number, tense, or voice.**

Example 1.  Donald became conceited after he had won the prize.

It would be incorrect to say "after the prize was won by him" in this sentence.

Example 2. Everyone in the group should have *his* papers ready.

The third-person pronoun *his* is correct in this sentence; "your papers" would be incorrect.

**248. Do not use "due to" as a preposition. "Due" is an adjective and should not be used to introduce a phrase that modifies a verb.**

Example 1. John's selection was due to his good record.

It would be incorrect to say, "John was selected due to his good record."

**249. In passing from one thought to another be sure to make the connection clear to the reader. The passage from one thought to another is called *transition*, and words, phrases, or clauses that make the transition clear are *transitional*.**

Example 1. Tom has very poor eyesight. In spite of this handicap, he has done extremely well in his studies.

These sentences would not be clear if they read: "Tom has very poor eyesight. He has done extremely well in his studies." The transitional phrase, *in spite of this handicap,* makes the connection clear.

# LETTER FORMS

## The Parts of a Letter

In all business letters and in formal social letters, there are six parts:

(1) the *heading,* which gives the writer's address and the date of his writing

(2) the *inner address,* which identifies the person to whom he is writing

(3) the *greeting,* which corresponds to a spoken "How do you do?"

(4) the *body,* which contains the writer's message

(5) the *close,* which corresponds to the spoken farewell

(6) the *signature,* which identifies the writer

Informal social letters omit the inner address, but they retain the other five parts.

The *heading* gives the writer's street address, the city and state, and the date. It is written on three lines, with the address above the date. The number of the postal zone, if any, immediately follows the name of the city. If the address is already printed on the letterhead, only the date is written. In an informal social note written to a correspondent to whom the writer's address is well known, the address may be omitted, leaving only the date.

The heading is placed one to two inches from the top of the sheet, depending upon the length of the letter, and slightly to the right of the center. The final letter or figure of the longest of the three lines should reach the right-hand margin of the letter. The form of the heading may be block or indented. In block form (see Business Letter, page 176) the second and third lines begin exactly beneath the first line, thus making the left-hand margin of the heading vertical. In indented form (see Formal Social Letter, page 177) both the second and third lines begin a few spaces to the right of the line above, thus making the left-hand margin diagonal. The block form is customary in typed letters, and the indented form is often found in pen-written communications.

## Business Letter

409 Monroe Street
Rockville, Maryland
May 17, 1943

Chadwick Berners Paper Company
268 South Broad Street
Philadelphia 30, Pennsylvania

Gentlemen:

In filling my order of May 10 for 12 reams of #2 white bond paper, priced at one dollar and seventy-five cents ($1.75), you sent me 15 reams. This, I think, was probably an error on the part of the stock clerk, since the additional packages were not noted on the invoice, No. 3672-G.

Since I have decided to keep the extra reams, I am enclosing a check for twenty-six dollars and twenty-five cents ($26.25), instead of for the amount of your bill.

Very truly yours,

Ray C. Black

End punctuation may be used in the heading, in which case a comma is placed after each of the first two lines, and a period at the close of the last. In open punctuation, which is more widely in use today, particularly with block form, no punctuation marks close the lines. In both forms, a comma must be inserted between the names of city and state, and between the figures for day and year.

Each word in the heading begins with a capital letter. Abbreviations are to be avoided except in the case of very long names; for example, *Portland, Maine*, should be spelled in full, but *Honolulu, Territory of Hawaii*, may be abbreviated to *Honolulu, T. H.* When streets are numbered, it is usual to spell out all those with numbers from one to ten, for example, 615 East Second Street.

## Formal Social Letter

767 Pine Hill Road,
Columbia, South Carolina,
February 14, 1943.

Mrs. Charles Randolph Lovell,
1256 Tudor Drive,
Chapel Hill, North Carolina.

My dear Mrs. Lovell,

The Altrusa Club of Columbia is looking forward with great interest to your lecture on February 22. It will give me, personally, additional pleasure to have the privilege of entertaining you informally in my home at a small dinner, following the lecture. There will be perhaps °ten or twelve guests, all congenial people and all vitally interested in the movement that you are sponsoring.

I believe that an informal exchange of ideas over the coffee cups afterward may help to sharpen the message you will have had for us in the afternoon.

Cordially yours,

Caroline March

(Mrs. Robert Beaufort March)

The *inner address* begins at the left margin of the letter, two lines below the heading. It is usually written in three lines and follows the form set by the heading, whether block or indented, with open or closed punctuation. A title (*Mr., Dr., Miss, Captain*) is always used with the name, followed by a period when the title is abbreviated, as in the case of the first two cited. The form and spelling of the name follow the addressee's own preference when this is known. If he is known to sign his name *Joe Hare*, or *Sam Browne*, the address is *Mr. Joe Hare*, or *Mr. Sam Browne*, not "Mr. Joseph Hare" nor "Mr. Samuel Browne." On the other hand, if these are nicknames reserved for friends, courtesy demands that the stranger use the full name.

The *greeting* begins two lines below the inner address, directly beneath the address and flush with the left-hand margin. In business letters to a firm, the phrasing is usually *Gentlemen* or *Dear Sirs*; to an individual, *Dear Sir* or *Dear Madam*; to an individual known personally to the writer, *Dear Miss Stone*; to a public official of high rank, as a senator or a governor, *Sir*. Business firms often use *Dear Mr. Jones* rather than *Dear Sir* when they wish to make the recipient feel that he is receiving individual attention.

In formal social letters, either *Dear Mr. Livingstone* or *My dear Mr. Livingstone* may be used, the latter indicating a more formal relationship than the former. In informal letters, *Dear* is used, followed by the name the person would use if addressing the person verbally; for example, *Dear John, Dear Mother,* or *Dear Mr. Poole.*

The first word and all names and titles in the greeting are capitalized; thus, *My dear Mr. Rush, Dear Sir,* and *Dear Aunt Helen.* In business letters a colon closes the greeting. In social letters a comma is used.

The *body* of the letter begins two lines below the greeting. The first line of each paragraph is indented a little, always to the same extent. All other lines are flush with the left-hand margin. The right-hand margin of the letter should be kept as even as possible by using hyphens to separate into syllables long words occurring at the ends of lines.

Crowding the letter into the upper half of the page should be avoided, as well as bringing it so near the bottom that signature and close are not given their proper allotment of space. Centering the letter on the page, allowing margins of one to two inches for sides and top, and of one to three inches for the bottom, produces an attractive, balanced page. Naturally, the shorter the letter, the wider the margins should be. Only one side of the paper is used in business and formal social letters. If the message takes more than a page to convey, use a second sheet (not a letterhead), and write at the top of it the number of the page, the name of the individual addressed, and the date; as, *2—Dr. Robert E. Keaton—June 30, 1943.*

The accepted rules of grammar, capitalization, and sentence structure apply to the body of the letter. Subjects and predicates must be expressed rather than implied in a business or formal social letter. To write "Wish to order a desk" is to indicate that the writer is either too busy or too indolent to write a complete sentence. Either condition is hardly complimentary to his correspondent. Concluding sentences should also be complete. Phrases such as "Thanking you in advance," "Trusting to hear from you soon," and "Begging to remain," are not in good usage. Trite expressions like "Wish to advise," "Contents duly noted," "Enclosed please find," "15th inst.," and "and oblige" should also be avoided.

It is desirable to give both figures and written words for prices and money enclosures; as, *I enclose a money order for two dollars and sixty cents ($2.60)*. This is particularly important in hand-written letters, since some individuals' handwriting is not easily read correctly.

Full information necessary for understanding a transaction, or for filling an order, must be supplied. Include specific details as to kind, size, amount, price, time limit for filling, author and title of books wanted, time and place for appointments, and any other items which clarify the message for the recipient and enable him to carry out the instructions. If the letter is a reply to an earlier communication, the date, subject, and file number of the earlier letter should be mentioned in order to insure prompt attention and satisfactory service. On the other hand, all details which have no bearing on the transaction should be excluded. The goal should be a brief, courteous communication which tells the receiver what he needs to know, but which wastes none of his time by causing him to read what does not pertain to the transaction.

Informal letters reflect the tone the writer would use in conversation with his correspondent. Ease and naturalness should mark such letters. Contractions (*I don't, he wouldn't*), colloquialisms, and slang are permitted to the extent that they would be in conversation. An occasional incomplete sentence for emphasis may also be used, provided the occurrence is not so frequent as to make the letter seem abrupt and choppy. Sentence monotony may often be avoided by varying the position of subordinate clauses or by using phrases at the beginning. Particularly to be avoided is a sequence of sentences beginning with "I." A letter which begins with an apology for not having written earlier gives an unfortunate impression. Unless the failure to write was a really serious matter, do not mention it.

The most enjoyable letters are those which give cheerful, vivid pictures of people or happenings of interest to the reader and which show most clearly the personality of the writer.

The *close* of a letter is placed two lines below the body and even with the first word of the heading. Only the first word is capitalized. The phrase is followed by a comma.

The words chosen for the close should be appropriate to the person addressed. Letters to public officials of high rank, or formal letters to superiors in general, may conclude with *Respectfully yours* or *Yours respectfully*. In business letters, if the greeting has been *Sir* or *Dear Sir*, the close is usually *Very truly yours* or *Yours very truly*. If the greeting has been *Dear Mrs. Smith*, the choice may be either *Very truly yours* or *Sincerely yours*. For formal social letters, use *Sincerely yours, Cordially yours,* or *Very truly yours*. Informal letters conclude with *Sincerely yours, Yours sincerely, With love,* or any other term typical of the relationship existing between the two correspondents.

The writer's *signature* is written two or three lines below the close. The signature begins even with the close if block form has been used in the heading and the inner address, or a little to the right of the close if indented form has been used. No title is used with the signature. However, in a business letter or in a formal social letter to strangers, an unmarried woman encloses her title in parentheses, as *(Miss) Margaret Cain*. An employed married woman, writing from her place of business, signs herself *(Mrs.) Mary C. Smith*. A married woman at home encloses her title and her husband's name beneath her own signature, as,

*Mary C. Smith*

*(Mrs. John G. Smith)*

A widow may use the same signature she used previous to her husband's death.

The signature should be legible to a reader who has not seen it before. In typed letters it is customary to type the writer's name four spaces below the close. If he is writing about the business of an organization, his position in the organization is noted on a fifth line. Immediately above the typed name, the writer's hand-written signature is placed. Letters which are not typed must, of course, depend upon the writer's ability to make his name readable. Some firms prefer to have the

## The Envelope

*John M. Black*
*1628 Prince George Street*
*Annapolis, Maryland*

> *Dr. Robert E. Keaton*
>
> *2108 Jackson Street*
>
> *Sioux City 18*
>
> *Iowa*

name of the firm typed in capital letters two lines below the closing, with the name of the writer four more lines below. His position may be indicated on the next line.

Informal social letters are often signed only with the writer's first name.

The *envelope* which encloses the letter bears in its upper left-hand corner the sender's name and address, written in three lines. Form and punctuation correspond to those followed in the heading, the inner address, and the close of the message. If block form has been used in the letter, block is also used for the return address. If indented form, with or without closed punctuation, has been used, that is also used in the return address.

The name and the address of the person to whom the letter is being sent are written, usually in four. lines, in the lower half of the envelope, either in the center or a little to the right of the center. The name is put on the first line, the street address on the second, the city and postal zone on the third, and the state on the fourth. Form and punctuation follow those of heading, inner address, close, and return address

**The individual's title is always used.** When the title is abbreviated, it is followed by a period, as *Capt., Dr.,* or *Mr.* A married woman addressed at her home is given her husband's name, as, *Mrs. John G. Smith.* But an employed married woman at her place of business is addressed as *Mrs. Mary C. Smith.* Except as in the examples mentioned under *inner address,* no nicknames or diminutives should be used on the envelope.

A letter is a substitute for a verbal message which the writer would probably convey orally if distance and time permitted. It is important, therefore, that the substitute message speak as clearly and convincingly for the writer as he could if he were at its destination in person. He should make it say exactly what he wants it to say, and he should make sure that its effect upon the recipient will be the one he wishes to produce. Form, punctuation, and sentence structure are the devices the writer depends upon in shaping his ideas for the letter. But the ideas must be organized according to a definite plan worked out in the writer's mind for making his message effective. For example, it is recognized that the opening paragraph should tell the reader what kind of letter he has received and what it is about. Since his first impression is important, it should be a favorable one. The closing paragraph leaves the most lasting impression; hence it should reinforce the main idea of the letter and impress upon the reader the action the writer wishes him to take, particularly if the matter is urgent. If the first draft of a letter does not seem to the writer to represent him adequately, he should revise it until he is satisfied.

# RECORD SHEET*

(This is a sample record sheet. Do not write on this sheet. In your notebook rule a sheet like this.)

Name_____

| Survey Test Score | Progress Test Score | | | Achievement Test Score |
|---|---|---|---|---|
| Part 1 _____ | 1 _____ | 5 _____ | 9 _____ | Part 1 _____ |
| Part 2 _____ | 2 _____ | 6 _____ | 10 _____ | Part 2 _____ |
| Part 3 _____ | 3 _____ | 7 _____ | 11 _____ | Part 3 _____ |
| Total _____ | 4 _____ | 8 _____ | 12 _____ | Total _____ |

| Exercise Page | Date | Number Wrong | Numbers and letters of the rules missed |
|---|---|---|---|
| Example | Sept. 15 | 6 | 21b, 21e |
| 4 | | | |
| 5 | | | |
| 6 | | | |
| 7 | | | |
| 8 | | | |
| 9 | | | |
| 10 | | | |
| 11 | | | |
| 12 | | | |
| 13 | | | |
| 14 | | | |
| 15 | | | |

* For explanation of how this record sheet is to be used, see pages x to **xii**.

# SELF-CORRECTION AND GUIDANCE SECTION

## Parts of Speech and Other Grammatical Terms

**Page 1**

Exercise 1. (Rules 5—10; 12—14)
*Nouns* (72, 73)
1. men, leader
2. Harry's, study, mathematics, electricity, job
3. course, principles
4. Ruth
5. Bob, score
6. reward, Mrs. Allen, return, papers

*Pronouns* (72, 73, 74, 75, 84, 85)
1. their
2. him, his
3. Everyone, who
4. I, she
5. he, he, anyone, you, me
6. that, she

*Verbs* (16, 18, 18a, 18b, 19)
1. listened, spoke
2. is helping
3. takes, learns
4. exclaimed, forgot, was
5. tries, makes, is playing
6. was offered, had lost

*Adjectives* (105, 106, 108)
1. The, excited
2. new
3. this, a, few, basic, mechanical
4. alone
5. a, high
6. a, large, the, the

*Adverbs* (107)
1. attentively
3. thoroughly
5. hard, never
6. carelessly

*Prepositions*
2. of, in
5. with, except
6. by, for, of

*Conjunctions* (83, 163, 164)
1. while
3. and
4. that
5. but, when, or

*Interjections*
4. Oh

**Page 2**

Exercise 2.
*Subjects* (1, 67, 69, 222, 222a)
7. My brother Charles
8. a girl from Indiana
9. All the men who had passed the test
10. Carlton and his brother
11. Whoever made this model

*Predicates* (1, 69, 222, 222a)
7. will write Harold a letter in a few days
8. Yesterday interviewed Mr. Sims about a job
9. went to the plant and began to work immediately
10. told us that they couldn't come to the meeting
11. is an expert craftsman and has real scientific ability

Exercise 3.
*Prepositional phrases* (10, 227)
7. in a few days
8. from Indiana, about a job
10. to the meeting
11. none
13. on Wednesday, before Monday

Exercise 4.
*Subordinate clauses* (2, 11, 84, 225, 226)
9. who had passed the test
10. that they couldn't come to the meeting
11. Whoever made this model
12. none
14. who has offered to show us how to repair the radio

184

**Page 3**

Exercise 5.
*Kind* (164a, 222, 223, 224)

| | |
|---|---|
| 7. simple | 12. compound |
| 8. simple | 13. compound |
| 9. complex | 14. complex |
| 11. complex | 15. compound |

Exercise 6.
*Direct objects* (15, 17a, 68, 69)
8. Mr. Sims
10. that they couldn't come to the meeting
11. (1) model (2) ability
12. (1) phonograph (2) records
13. (1) shipment (2) delivery

Exercise 7.
*Indirect objects* (68)
7. Harold
10. us
12. (1) Florence (2) her
13. you
14. us

Exercise 8.
*Predicate nominative* (71)
11. craftsman
14. Ferris
15. stenographer

**Page 3, Cont'd**

Exercise 9.
*Tenses* (7, 18, 18b, 19, 20)
7. will write (future)
9. had passed (past perfect)
went (past)
began (past)
11. made (past)
is (present)
has (present)
13. had expected (past perfect)
can promise (present)
14. has offered (present perfect)
is (present)
15. will be (future)
will be (future)
wants (present)

Exercise 10.
*Infinitives* (19a)
9. to work
10. none
12. to play
14. (1) to show (2) to repair
15. to apply

# Drills

**Page 4**
1. gone 21b
2. come 21a
3. run 21a
4. eaten 21b
5. sang 21a
6. broken 21e
7. drawn 21d
8. saw 21b
9. grown 21d
10. chosen 21e
11. did 21b
12. frozen 21e
13. begun 21a
14. ridden 21c
15. did 21b
16. known 21d
17. spoken 21e
18. taken 21c

**Page 5**
1. worn 21f
2. brought 22
3. set 26a
4. said 23a
5. drank 21a
6. sat 26
7. torn 21f
8. eaten 21b
9. started 23a
10. sit 26
11. come 21a
12. brought 22
13. set 26a
14. given 21c
15. used 23a
16. saw 21b
17. sat 26
18. brought 22
19. broken 21e

**Page 5, Cont'd**
20. set 26a
21. sworn 21f
22. sit 26
23. brought 22
24. asked 23a
25. known 21d
26. sits 26
27. torn 21f

**Page 6**
1. let 27
2. Lie 30
3. teach 28
4. rise 29
5. let 27
6. ran 21a
7. lay 30
8. brought 22

**Page 6, Cont'd**
9. raised 29a
10. eaten 21b
11. teach 28
12. worn 21f
13. Let 27
14. rising 29
15. threw 21d
16. let 27
17. lying 30
18. teach 28
19. worn 21f
20. said 23, 23a
21. lay 30
22. learn 28
23. sitting 26
24. started 23, **23a**
25. let 27
26. rose 29
27. given 21c

**Page 7**
1. worn 21f
2. has 39
3. rung 21a
4. C
5. C
6. There are 39
7. C
8. were 36
9. C
10. C
11. doesn't 37
12. saw 21b
13. C
14. spoken 21e
15. let 27
    began 21a
16. C
17. gives 36
18. C
19. sang 21a
20. C
21. frozen 21e

**Page 8**
1. is 40, 40a
2. aren't 59
3. spoke 21e
4. have 61
5. Can't 58
6. drawn 21d
7. ought 60
8. has 40a
9. let 27
10. gone 21b
11. Aren't 59
12. swore 21f
13. wasn't 58
14. ought not 60
15. rode 21c
16. was 40a
17. said 23a
18. don't 36, 38
19. ought 60
20. were 38
21. ought 60
22. lying 30
23. keeps 40a
24. seen 21b
25. couldn't 58
26. grew 21d
27. isn't 59

**Page 9**
1. asked 23, 23a
2. lain 30
3. ought 60
4. let 27
5. knew 21d
6. drunk 21a
7. taught 28
8. isn't 59
9. worn 21f
10. were 38a
11. are 38
12. rang 21a
13. live 40a
14. taken 21c
15. rise 29
16. did 21b
17. were 39
18. stolen 21e
19. doesn't 37
20. given 21c
21. won't 58
22. sung 21a
23. written 21c

**Page 10**
1. chose 21e
   (has chosen)
2. C 21b
3. teach 28
4. torn 21f
5. were 36, 38
6. written 21c
7. are 39
8. said 23a
9. doesn't 37
10. C 21b
11. worn 21f
    (Omit *have*.)
12. C 29a
13. doesn't 37
14. gave 23a
15. were 38
16. Omit *had*. 60
17. C 26a
18. lay 30
19. began 21a
20. seem 36
21. have 40a
22. Are 39
    (Omit *has*.)
23. drawn 21d
24. C 38

**Page 11**
1. come 21a
2. C 29
3. sworn 21f
4. C 30a
5. taken 21c
6. were 38a
7. taught 28
8. chosen 21e
9. are 38
10. were 39
11. doesn't 37
12. Omit *had*. 60
13. C 40a
14. ought not 60
    (oughtn't)
15. grown 21d
16. were 38
17. let 27
18. worn 21f
19. C 38a
20. ate 23a
21. doesn't 37
22. rang 21a
23. C 26a
24. knew 21d
25. C 30
26. given 21c
27. thinks 40a

**Page 12**
1. Doesn't 37
2. taught 28
3. grew 21d
4. have 36, 38
5. swore 21f
6. C 39
7. sang 21a
8. were 36, 38
9. Omit *had*. 60
10. C 21e
11. raised 29a
12. don't 36, 38
13. have 61
14. C 30a
15. Have 36, 38
16. doesn't 37
17. known 21d
18. lay 30
19. let 27
20. were 38a
21. came 23a
22. lay 30

***Page 12, Cont'd***
23. am I not 59
24. spoken 21e
25. C 36, 38
26. stolen 21e
27. C 27a

**Page 13**
1. came 23a
2. sit 26
3. rose 29
4. brought 22
   (brings)
5. leave 36
6. taken 21c
7. let 27
8. are 39
9. frozen 21e
10. laid 30a
11. have 61
12. ran 21a
13. were 38a
14. Omit *had*. 60
15. said 23a
16. worn 21f
17. threw 21d
18. lying 30
19. have 38
20. set 26a
21. gone 21b
    (Omit *has*.)
22. were 40a
23. Wasn't 58
24. doesn't 37

**Page 14**
1. we 77
2. him 79
3. me 80
4. They 77, 78
5. He 77
6. me 79
7. You and he 77,
   77a
8. I 77
9. me 80
10. Them 79
11. Those 78
12. me 79
13. He and I 77
14. him 79
15. He and she 77
16. You, Mary, and
    I 77a

**Page 14, Cont'd**

17. us 79
18. them 79
19. me 80
20. him 79
21. her 80
22. you and her 79
23. she 77
24. Those 77, 78

**Page 15**

1. me 81, 81a
2. We 82
3. her 81
4. us 82a
5. I 77
6. me 81a
7. us 79
8. him and her 81
9. us 82a
10. They 78
11. him 81a
12. The Whites and we 77a
13. him and me 81
14. him and me 79
15. We 82
16. her 81a
17. him 79
18. us 82a
19. They 78
20. them and us 81
21. she 77
22. us 82a
23. us 81a
24. him 79
25. us 82a
26. We 82
27. him and her 81

**Page 16**

1. George 95
2. us 82b
3. them 79
4. himself 96
5. She and I 77
6. them and us 81
7. us 82b
8. themselves 96
9. him 79
10. those 78
11. me 81a
12. me 81

**Page 16, Cont'd**

13. Machinists 95
14. himself 96
15. us 82b
16. My sister and I 77, 77a
17. us 82a
18. them 79
19. her and me 79
20. themselves 96
21. them 81a
22. her 81
23. himself 96
24. us 82a
25. us 82b
26. We 82
27. Mrs. Gray 95

**Page 17**

1. him 81a
2. saw 21b
3. I 77
4. sat 26
5. gave 23a
6. us 82a
7. written 21c
8. Those 78
9. C 82b
10. run 21a
11. let 27
12. them 79
13. worn 21f
14. us 82a
15. C 30
16. Omit *he*. 95
17. C 36
18. themselves 96
19. those 78
20. C 29
21. him and me 80
22. C 79
23. setting 26a
24. Omit *they*. 95
25. C 82
26. themselves 96
27. aren't 59

**Page 18**

1. captain's 100
2. They and we 77
3. drivers' 100a
4. us 82b
5. her 79

**Page 18, Cont'd**

6. friends' 100a
7. himself 96
8. Lewis's 100
9. The children 95
10. James's 100
11. us 79
12. players' 100a
13. they 78
14. customers' 100a
15. her 81a
16. nurse's 100
17. us 82a
18. He and I 77
19. me 81
20. us 82b
21. horse's 100
22. us 82a
23. carpenters' 100a
24. them 79
25. brakeman's 100
26. him and her 80
27. welders' 100a

**Page 19**

1. women's 100b
2. himself 96
3. yours 102
4. us 82a
5. I 77
6. Jones's 100
7. us 82b
8. salesmen's 100b
9. we 82
10. its 102
11. him 81a
12. stenographers' 100a
13. him and me 80
14. men's 100b
15. me 79
16. Ferguson's 100
17. us 82b
18. him 81
19. Whose 102
20. us 82a
21. employees' 100a
22. He and she 77
23. Colonel Bush 95
24. theirs 102
25. mice's 100b
26. him and me 81a
27. me 79

**Page 20**

1. theirs 102
2. I 77
3. him 81
4. Jane 95
5. golfers' 100a
6. themselves 96
7. Rose and I 77a
8. him 79
9. us 82a
10. him 80
11. they 78
12. women's 100b
13. me 81a
14. we 82
15. William's 100
16. us 82b
17. me 81a
18. me 80
19. him 81
20. me 82a
21. she 82
22. its 102
23. me 82b

**Page 21**

1. themselves 96
2. C 100b
3. We 82
4. hers 102
5. her 79
6. C 100b
7. me 81
8. applicants' 100a
9. C 81a
10. its 102
11. I 77
12. C 81
13. C 82b
14. himself 96
15. them 79
16. us 82a
17. C 100
18. girls' 100a
19. Omit *she*. 95
20. C 100
21. C 78
22. C 100b
23. her 81a
24. her 79
25. C 102
26. we 77
27. operators' 100a

## Page 22

1. C 79
2. us 82b
3. Omit *he*. 95
4. us 80
5. C 100
6. C 79
7. her 81a
8. we 77
9. C 82a
10. C 81
11. themselves 96
12. C 79
13. stonemasons' 100a
14. me 81a
15. them 81
16. saleswomen's 100b
17. Black's 100
18. us 81
19. yours 102
20. mechanics' 100a
21. us 82b
22. geese's 100b
23. us 82a
24. C 79
25. himself 96
26. her and me 80
27. we 82

## Page 23

1. C 102
2. Jim and I 77, 77a
3. C 81
4. himself 96
5. C 100
6. him 81a
7. Green's 100
8. C 100b
9. him 79
10. ours 102
11. us 82b
12. them 80
13. doctors' 100a
14. us 82a
15. her 79
16. men's 100b
17. C 82
18. C 77
19. themselves 96
20. C 81a

## Page 23, Cont'd

21. her and me 79
22. women's 100b
23. me 80
24. me 81a
25. hers 102
26. C 100b
27. theirs 102

## Page 24

1. he 77
2. me 81a
3. Those 78 (These)
4. volunteers' 100a
5. us 82a
6. him 79
7. themselves 96
8. Charles's 100
9. me 80
10. Omit *he*. 95
11. ours 102
12. C 100b
13. We 82
14. me 80
15. he 77
16. us 82a
17. her 81
18. buyers' 100a
19. us 82b
20. women's 100b
21. C 82a
22. her 79
23. those 78 (they) (these)
24. its 102

## Page 25

1. well 111
2. cordial 116
3. quickly 110
4. fresh and clean 117
5. steadily 116a
6. well 111
7. easily 110
8. quiet 116
9. well 111
10. cheerfully 110
11. good 117
12. suddenly 116a
13. close 117

## Page 25, Cont'd

14. well 111
15. considerably 110
16. well 111
17. badly 110
18. uneasy 117
19. bravely 110
20. gruff 116
21. well 111
22. more roughly 110
23. excellent 116
24. correct 116

## Page 26

1. an 124
2. neater 118
3. more lightly 110
4. that 130
5. steadily 117a
6. urgent 117
7. an 124
8. better 118
9. well 111
10. this 130
11. listlessly 117a
12. a 124
13. better 118
14. more quickly 116a
15. this 130
16. normally 110
17. An 124 an 124
18. worse 118
19. more nearly 110
20. this 130
21. blankly 117a
22. an 124
23. distinctly 117a
24. that 130
25. longer 118
26. An 124

## Page 27

1. anywhere 133
2. an 124
3. two 136
4. This 131
5. anything 133
6. this 130
7. These 132

## Page 27, Cont'd

8. bigger 118
9. too 136
10. strongly 117a
11. Those 132
12. had 133
13. would 133
14. an 124
15. these 131
16. two 136 too 136
17. is 133
18. those 132
19. these 130
20. Two 136
21. Those 131
22. too 136
23. had 133
24. more quickly 110
25. those 132
26. too 136

## Page 28

1. C
2. its 102
3. seem 36
4. C
5. that 130
6. teachers' 100a
7. C
8. me 80
9. have 61
10. C
11. me 81a
12. attractive 117
13. let 27
14. don't 58
15. lie 30 is 40a
16. Omit *had*. 60
17. C
18. C
19. normally 110
20. C
21. too 136
22. C

## Page 29

1. going 141
2. at home 147
3. from 144
4. be 141

**Page 29, Cont'd**

5. at home 147
6. from 144
7. were you 141
8. had 146
9. from 144
10. at home 147
11. gone 141
12. at home 147
13. from 144
14. had 146
15. go 141
16. from 144
17. had 146
18. be 141
19. from 144
20. at home 147
21. had 146

**Page 30**

1. cheerful 117
2. a 124
3. those 132
4. switch 141
5. ordinarily 116a
6. at home 147
7. sharper 118
8. two 136
9. well 111
10. had 146
11. that 131
12. angry 116
13. suddenly 117a
14. from 144
15. anybody 133
16. easily 110
17. that 130
18. fragrant 117
19. considerate 116
20. well 111
21. strongly 117a
22. more clearly 110

**Page 31**

1. smooth 117
2. those 132
   (these)
3. were 39
4. C 81a
5. too 136
6. C 130
7. used 23a
8. anything 133
   (was nothing)

**Page 31, Cont'd**

9. C 77
10. from 144
11. Omit *there*. 131
12. at home 147
13. C 110
14. Omit *to*. 141
15. girls' 100a
16. Omit *of*. 146
17. us 82b
18. were 38a
19. that 130
20. at home 147
21. anywhere 133
22. cashier's 100
23. two 136
24. C 21a
25. Omit *there*. 131
26. aren't 58

**Page 32**

1. anything 133
2. had used 146
3. well 111
4. Omit *more*. 118
5. Omit *here*. 131
6. tardy, too 136
7. C 130
8. C 110
9. easily 110
10. those 132
11. C 117a
12. could have 133
13. an honorable 124
14. quickly 116a
15. was no 133
   (wasn't any)
16. badly 110
17. from 144
18. Omit *there*. 131
19. smart 117
20. could have 133
21. more easily 110
22. strong 117
23. strongly 117a
24. at home 147
25. ever 133

**Page 33**

1. Omit *more*. 118
2. anybody 133
   (was nobody)

**Page 33, Cont'd**

3. C 110
4. from 144
5. sweet 117
6. well 111
7. Omit *there*. 131
8. Omit *of*. 146
9. two 136
10. dark and forbidding 116
11. those 132
12. worse 118
13. well 111
14. at home 147
15. happy 117
16. any 133
17. C 117
18. Omit *of*. 146
19. a 124
20. Omit *at*. 141
21. more sternly 110
22. this 130
23. from 144
24. frequently 116a

**Page 34**

1. Viennese 180
2. He 177
3. S. T. 182
4. Kentuckian 181
5. And 183
6. Henry Grey 178
   British Isles 178
7. Spanish 181a
8. Indian 180
9. Did 177
10. American Library Association 179
11. Italian 181a
12. United States 178
    St. Augustine 178
13. Ingersoll 178a
14. Federalists 181
15. Society for the Prevention of Cruelty to Animals 179
16. C.I.O. 182

**Page 34, Cont'd**

17. Swan 178a
    Ivory 178a
18. French 180
19. T. S. Eliot 178
20. Buddhists 181

**Page 35**

1. West 187
2. Here 184
3. *Millions of Cats* 188
4. Federal Security Agency 179, 190
   Baltimore 178
5. Easter 185
6. King 189
   Queen 189
7. "that 184a
8. summer 186
9. Who 183
   'This 183
10. Bishop 189
11. west 187
12. *Gone with the Wind* 188
    summer 186
13. doctor 189a
    Mayor 189
14. "They 184a
15. South 187
16. Senate 178
17. winters 186
18. captain 189a
19. *The Pines of Rome* 188
20. "We 184
21. Admiral 189
22. N.E.A. 182
23. Day 185
    Christmas 185
24. "The 184
25. east 187

**Page 36**

1. Sir 189
   Francis Drake 178
2. spring 186
3. I 194
4. Clubs 190, 179
5. "as 184a
6. Tuesday 185

## Page 36, Cont'd

7. Lake Champlain 190
8. "When 184
9. Constitution 191
10. *The Moon Is Down* 188
11. Librarian of Congress 189b
12. Portuguese 181a
13. Spirit 192
    Creator 192
    Sovereign 192
14. Pentateuch 193
    Old Testament 193
15. Democrats 181
    aldermen 189a
16. Brazilian 187
    North American 180
17. Union Pacific Railroad 190
18. W. W. 182
19. Eveready 178a
20. Uncle 189
21. Ambassador 189b
    President 189b
22. We 177

## Page 37

1. Secretary of the Navy 189b
2. "There 184
3. Put 177
4. *Twelve Men in a Box* 188
5. Magna Charta 191
6. *The Thinker* 188
7. fall 186
8. Charter 191
9. Empire State Building 190, 178
10. North Americans 177, 181
    South Americans 181

## Page 37, Cont'd

11. Genesis 193
12. uncle 189a
13. American 180, 181
14. North 187
    winter 186
15. Latin 181a
16. River 190
17. "Now 184a, 177
18. Lieutenant Commander 189
19. "R. N." 182
20. C 185
21. Said 183
22. American Chemical Society 179, 190

## Page 38

1. saw which we 195
2. pliers, hammers, chisels, 200
3. Thursday? 197
4. Fla., 196
    Ill., 196
5. What! 198a
    Never! 198a
6. Mr. 196
    Mrs. 196
7. doctor 196a
8. C 200
9. Oh! 198a
    machine! 198
10. require. 197
11. lawn, 200
    hedge, 200
12. answered! 198
13. pages, 200
    them, 200
14. untwisting. 197
15. vise in 195
16. F.B.I. 196 (FBI)
17. chisel. 197
18. simple, flexible, 200
19. o'clock when 195
20. position! 198

## Page 39

1. "I—blankets." 214
2. Aires, Argentina, 206
    Philadelphia, 206
3. No, 210
4. E. L. Glenn, Sr., 196
5. you, Mrs. White, 211
6. "I—right." 214
7. radio! 198
8. Omit quotation marks. 215
9. Yes, 210
10. register? 197
11. Lisbon, Portugal, 206
    Friday, June 4, 207
12. "It—work," 214
13. Springfield, 206
14. seen; 212
15. job, 211
16. Yes, 210
17. Omit quotation marks. 215
18. Oh! 198a
19. door, 200
    garden, 200
20. switch; 212
21. "Open—broken," 214
22. Monday, May 5, 207
    Williamsburg, 206
23. No, 210

## Page 40

1. now," 218
2. please." 220
3. message,"— "as 216
4. said. 219
5. butchers!" 220
6. come,"— "please 216
7. wire!" 218
8. "You—come," 214

## Page 40, Cont'd

9. said. 219
10. time?' " 220
11. McKinley," 218 read, 219
12. Monday,—6, 1953, 207
13. Omit quotation marks. 215
14. said, 219
15. vaccine,"— "which 216
16. finished?" 218
17. said. 219
18. Annapolis, 206
19. think, Carl, 211
20. harden?" 218
21. lumber,"—"as 216
22. dead"? 220
23. binder; 212

## Page 41

1. called,"—"to 216
2. number, 211
3. radio," 220
4. Omit quotation marks. 215
5. windows, 200 doors, 200
6. Ave., 196 D.C. 196
7. O.P.A. 196 (OPA)
8. in! 198
9. duckbill," 218 explained, 219
10. cord since 195
11. dictation! 198
12. March 15, 207
13. New Orleans, Louisiana, 206
14. Great!" 198a, 220
15. Well, 210
16. "I—assignment," 214
17. works. 197
18. "You— through." 214
19. captain 196a
20. last?" 218, 220

**Page 41, Cont'd**

21. C 197
22. asked, 219
    safe?" 220

**Page 42**

1. rusty because 195
2. Tomorrow, Lois, 211
3. Colorado," 218
4. Omit quotation marks. 215
5. farm, 200 lake, 200
6. "Two—five," 214
7. monthly; 212
8. wire because 195
9. Carl, 211
10. Omit quotation marks. 215

**Page 42, Cont'd**

11. high. 197
12. captain 196a
13. Wednesday, 207
14. "All—level," 214
15. Well, 210
16. dishes, 200 them, 200
17. heavens!" 198a salt?" 220
18. used even 195
19. hammer. 197
20. C 207
21. telephone, by letter, 200
22. it!" 218

**Page 43**

1. Colonial 180
2. C
3. food. 195
4. He 177

**Page 43, Cont'd**

5. C
6. French 180, 181
7. Robert Morris, 178
8. American Revolution 191
   Declaration of Independence 191
9. C
10. tea, 200 cream, 200
11. "Pray, 214 sir, 211 tea," 220
12. "No, 210 Mr. Morris," 218 reply, 219 "although 216

**Page 43, Cont'd**

13. C
14. "What, sir! 211, 198a hospitality?" 220
15. protest. 195
16. European 180
17. C
18. Minute Men 179 Concord, 178, 206 Massachusetts, 178
19. Omit quotation mark. 215
20. Mr. Morris 189b, 178
21. Omit quotation mark. 215

**Page 44***

1. sold to a doctor a car missing 233
2. overflowing; he 229 (overflowing, and)
3. Supply principal clause. 228
4. Make separate sentences. 231 (Dinner—night, we—afterward, and then—telephone. Consequently)
5. again without 228
6. me while 228
7. Supply principal clause. 228
8. Cannon, so 229 (Cannon; he)
9. I—operator. However, she—in and did not—name. That is why—information. 231
10. Friday because 228
11. Show relation. 231 (When the baby—over, the dog excitedly ran—ink, tracking it—rug.)
12. woman's green 233
13. present, although 228, 229
14. recognized from his picture in the paper the man 233

**Page 45**

1. thin; it 229 (thin, and)
2. doomed even 228
3. Show relation. 231 (She nervously fingered her neck-lace until the thread)
4. worn; it 229 (worn, and)
5. Show relation. 231 (When we—factory, just as the whistle was blowing, we)
6. brake with all 233
7. curb; the 229 (curb, and)
8. Supply subject. 228
9. Show relation. 231 (Mother put into a wooden box—closet some oily rags she had been using in cleaning, and probably)
10. listed for rent to a gentleman a room with 233

*Some of the sentence-structure items in this book may, of course, be corrected in ways other than those given in the key. A change that makes the sentence correct and preserves its meaning should be given credit even though it does not appear in the key. It is desirable, however, that the correction indicated by the rule reference be understood, in order that the student may master the principle.

**Page 45, Cont'd**

11. Make separate sentences. 231
    (When the—rang, Bob—Betty. He
    wanted—first, so—phone, but)
12. ready; —bought; 229
    (ready, —bought, and)
13. here on his motorcycle to get 233
14. Make separate sentences. 231
    (The window—paint, and—it. We
    —hard, but—mistake, for—broke.)
15. week without 228
16. Supply principal clause. 228
17. hole; the 229
    (hole, and)
18. Supply predicate. 228
19. shoes which 228

**Page 46**

1. Episcopalians 181
2. C 215
3. nonsense!" 198, 220
4. C 191, 207
5. No, 210
6. Monday—Tuesday—November 185
7. receipt whether 228
8. lieutenant 189a, 196a
9. Cairo, Illinois, 206
   Cairo, Egypt. 206
10. does.' " 220
11. dimmed, —slowly, 229
12. *A Tale of Two Cities* 188
13. Chicago Athletic Club 179, 190
14. nails, tools, 200
15. Show relation. 231
    (Mary wrote to her aunt, Sarah
    Hudson, who lived in Boston, ask-
    ing permission—overnight.)
16. C 180
17. Lux 178a
18. friends, 211
19. summer 186
20. meet. 197
21. declared, 219
22. Supply principal clause. 228

**Page 47**

1. Make separate sentences. 231
   (Shirley—dress and a brown one,
   too. She—buy, yet she—both.)
2. Argentinian 180
3. Yes, 210
4. C 188

**Page 47, Cont'd**

5. customer, and 229
   (customer; I)
6. Elsie and I 178, 194
7. Friday—Monday 185
8. inaccurate. 197
9. Omit quotation marks. 215
10. land"? 220
11. Spring 186
12. West 187
13. Men, 211
14. Albany, although 195, 228, 229
15. rooms,—baths,—garage, 200
16. C 219
17. Boston, Massachusetts, 206
18. captains 189a
19. brigadier general 196a, 189a
20. Thursday, December 31, 1942, 207
21. "but—play." 216
22. stenographer?" 218
23. *Nine* 188
24. children's woolen 233

**Page 48**

1. C
2. store. 197
3. well 116
   satisfactory 117
4. weeks' 100a
5, 6, 7, 8. doesn't 37
   hum, squeal, 200
   A friend of mine who—radio checked
   —wires. Since—trouble, he advised me to lay the matter in your
   hands. 231, 30a
9, 10. carry 36
   Omit quotation marks. 215
11. can't 58
    to 136
12. is 40a
13. set? 197
    I 77
    Omit *had*. 60
    at 147
14. let 27
15. sitting 26
16, 17. wonder, when—up, in whose—
    made. 233, 102
    you that 228
18. Club 190
19. me 81
20. Friday, 207

## Page 49

1. may 31
2. has worked 24
3. was 40b
4. is 42
5. affected 32
6. is 42
7. has been 24
8. extends 42a
9. can 31
10. are 40b
11. was 25
12. was 42
13. excepted 33
14. might 31
15. was 42
16. was 42a
17. may 31
18. is 42a
19. has 40b
20. affected 32

## Page 50

1. contains 50
2. look 45
3. is 40b
4. is 50
5. have served 24
6. were 55
7. see 51
8. were 25
9. had 54
10. was 42
11. understand 51
12. hadn't 54
13. are 45
14. has 50
15. should 56
16. were 55
17. were 45
18. admires 42a
19. would 56a
20. have 51
21. would 56a
22. should 56

## Page 51

1. accepted 33
2. shall 57
3. should 56
4. would 56a
5. might 57
6. should 56

## Page 51, Cont'd

7. Shall 62b
8. would 56a
9. will 57
10. Shall 62b
11. cast 64
12. were 51
13. forecast 64
14. shall 62b
15. could 57
16. Shall 62b
17. burst 64
18. effected 32
19. cast 64
20. had 54

## Page 52

1. were 55
2. burst 64
3. may 31
4. visited 25
5. has 42a
6. are 51
7. observes 40b
8. would 56a
9. has remained 24
10. is 50
11. had 54
12. have 45
13. should 56
14. shall 62b
15. is 42
16. may 57
17. excepted 33
18. effected 32

## Page 53

1. has shown 24
2. Shall 62b
3. belongs 42
4. Omit *have*. 25
5. is 42a
6. hadn't been 54
7. C 45
8. burst 64
9. C 40b
10. is 50
11. were 55
12. who have 51
13. should 56
14. C 42a
15. could 57

## Page 53, Cont'd

16. C 56a
17. may 31
18. has 40b
19. C 42a
20. C 55
21. shall 62b

## Page 54

1. may 31
2. has been sal-
   vaging 24
   (has salvaged)
3. Omit *of*. 54
4. C 62b
5. would 56a
6. saw 25
7. C 42a
8. agrees 40b
9. affects 32
10. recast 64
11. would 57
12. was 42
13. C 50
14. C 55
15. are 45
16. Omit *of*. 54
17. should 56
18. accepted 33
19. punches 42a
20. plays 51
21. could 57

## Page 55

1. her 81b
2. I 77b
3. them 83
4. who 84a
5. whom 84b
6. I 77b
7. I 83
8. him 81b
9. who 84a
10. whom 84b
11. her 81b
12. they 77b
13. her 83
14. him 81b
15. whom 84b
16. who 84a
17. he 77b
18. whom 84b
    whom 84b

## Page 55, Cont'd

19. who 84a
20. him and me 81b
21. we 77b
22. them 81b

## Page 56

1. who 93
2. she 77b
3. but 94
4. who 93, 93a
5. us 81b
6. which 93a
7. Peter the
   Great's 101
8. which 93
9. Tom's and Ed's
   101b
10. which 93a
11. whom 84b
12. Kaufman and
    Connelly's
    101a
13. John's and
    Bob's 101b
14. commissioner
    of deeds' 101
15. Brazil's and
    Peru's 101b
16. her 81b
17. who 93
18. son-in-law's
    101
19. that 93a
20. Parker and
    Lane's 101a
21. whom 84b
22. Mother's and
    daughter's
    101b

## Page 57

1. him 81b
2. but 94
3. Chief of Staff's
   101
4. I 77b
5. who 84a
6. Fred and
   Alice's 101b
7. which 93a
8. he 83

### Page 57, Cont'd

9. Husband's and wife's 101b
10. whom 84b
11. that 93
12. I 77b
13. who 84a
14. I 83
15. him 81b
16. which 93a
17. Walton and Hall's 101b
18. whom 84b
19. that 93

### Page 58

1. C 81b
2. have been reading 24 (have read)
3. John's 101b
4. C 55
5. that 93
6. C 42
7. C 101
8. had 54
9. they 83
10. hope 40b
11. Shall 62b
12. C 77b
13. that 93a
14. Butler and Wilcox's 101a
15. might 31
16. had oiled 54
17. admires 42a
18. him 81b
19. who 84a
20. C 57
21. I 77b
22. whom 84b
23. should 56
24. C 77b

### Page 59

1. Mr. Hale's 101b
2. C 84a
3. they 77b
4. that 93
5. whom 84b
6. she 83

### Page 59, Cont'd

7. who 93
8. I 83
9. her 81b
10. father-in-law's 101
11. that 93a
12. him 81b
13. but 94 (and)
14. whom 84b
15. C 81b
16. Gilbert and Sullivan's 101a
17. squirrels' 101b
18. we 77b
19. who 93a
20. C 101a
21. who 84a
22. I 77b
23. we 83

### Page 60

1. surely 112
2. as far as 121
3. and 126
4. really 113
5. and the 125
6. as long as 121
7. certainly 112
8. Almost 114
9. somewhat 115
10. and a 125
11. really 113
12. as far as 121
13. Almost 114
14. surely 112
15. somewhat 115
16. really 113
17. and 126
18. somewhat 115
19. extremely 113
20. almost 114
21. and the 125
22. certainly 112
23. Almost 114
24. very 113

### Page 61

1. was 133a
2. certainly 112
3. and a 127
4. of 129

### Page 61, Cont'd

5. than 128
6. somewhere 135
7. as far as 121
8. than 128
9. and a 127
10. and 126
11. of 129
12. rather 134
13. than a 128a
14. and a 125
15. rather 134
16. had 133a
17. than 128
18. of 129
19. very 113
20. and a 127
21. nowhere 135
22. than 128
23. somewhat 134
24. somewhere 135
25. hardly 133a
26. than 128
27. Almost 114

### Page 62

1. really 113
2. is 40b
3. Omit *a*. 129
4. she 77b
5. C 83, 77b
6. had 133a
7. and the 127
8. C 55
9. whom 84b
10. somewhat 115
11. rather 134 (somewhat) (a little)
12. Shall 62b
13. but 94
14. C 101b
15. were 45
16. the treasurer 125
17. almost 114
18. C 84a
19. Chief of Maintenance's 101
20. thinks 42a
21. C 93
22. Omit second *a*. 128

### Page 62, Cont'd

23. whom 93

### Page 63

1. wants to come in 142
2. off 145
3. Besides 155
4. like 143
5. remember 140
6. off 145
7. wants 143
8. Besides 155
9. remember 140
10. like 143
11. recollect 140
12. Beside 155
13. off 145
14. wanted to come in 142
15. wants 143
16. off 145
17. recall 140
18. wanted to go out 142
19. Besides 155
20. want 143
21. remember 140

### Page 64

1. Besides 155
2. by 160
3. by 158
4. recollect 140
5. within 156
6. with 160
7. by 158
8. off 145
9. Besides 155
10. within 156
11. of 162
12. by 158
13. like 143
14. with 160
15. with 161
16. of 162
17. with 161
18. of 162
19. wanted to get off 142
20. from 161
21. by 160
22. by 158
23. Within 156

**Page 65**

1. might 31
2. he 83
3. Omit second *a.* 128
4. Omit *of.* 140
5. and an 127
6. whom 84b
7. are 45
   (Omit second *a.* 127a)
8. extremely 113
   (very)
   (really)
9. Omit *of.* 145
10. Besides 155
11. of 162
12. is 40b
13. was 42a
14. has 42
15. Omit *for.* 143
16. anywhere 135
17. C 160
18. than a 128a
19. were 55
20. C 84a
21. Within 156
22. Omit *a.* 129
23. Omit *of.* 140
24. from 161

**Page 66**

1. but 164b
2. Unless 166
3. that 168
4. as 165
5. that 169
6. except that 167
7. as 165
8. as though 165
9. that 169
10. except that 167
11. as 165
12. except that 167
13. as 165
14. that 169
15. as 165
16. but 164b
17. unless 166
18. that 168
19. as though 165
20. unless 166

**Page 67**

1. because 170
2. except that 167
3. or 171a
4. That 173
5. that 168
6. nor 171
7. that 173a
8. because 170
9. That 173
10. except that 167
11. or 171a
12. that 173a
13. nor 171
14. when 176
15. nor ,71
16. as if 165
17. That 173
18. because 170
19. when 176
20. that 173a
21. except that 167

**Page 68**

1. really 113
2. recall 140
3. Surely 112
4. as if 165
5. Within 156
6. but 164b
7. and a 125
8. to see 143
9. almost 114
10. and a 127
11. nor 171
12. by 158
13. of 129
14. that 168
15. from 161
16. rather 134
17. was 133a
18. of 162
19. somewhere 135
20. except that 167
21. that 173a
22. Because 170

**Page 69**

1. of 162
2. to come in 142
3. as though 165
4. except that 167

**Page 69, Cont'd**

5. very 113
   (especially)
6. and an 125
7. Besides 155
8. surely 112
   (certainly)
9. C 171a
10. unless 166
11. the used 127
12. Omit *of.* 140
13. somewhat 115
    (a little)
    (rather)
14. than listener 128
15. Omit *for.* 143
16. within 156
17. C 158
18. a man 128a
19. that 173a
20. but 164b
21. the stenographer 125
22. when 176
23. with 161
24. that 169

**Page 70**

1. plan, we thought, 205
2. present, 199
3. long, narrow, 201
4. inaugurated, 203
5. find, he felt sure, 205
6. Brewster, 204
7. blind, 203
8. C 205
9. have, 199
10. C 201
11. ring, a— diamonds, 204
12. unit, 203
13. C 200, 201
14. Lewis, the— commentator, 204
15. clerks, he estimated, 205
16. C 203
17. smooth, 201

**Page 71**

1. "Sea Fever," 221
2. Omit comma. 201
3. said, 'Return— stock,' 217
4. C 213
5. spend,— authorities, 205
6. said, 'I like skating,' and I said, 'So do I,' 217
7. Omit comma. 208
8. these : 213
9. "Essay on Roast Pig" 221
10. Omit comma. 209
11. month, he decided, 205
12. Mann, 204
13. Omit comma. 208
14. said, 'You— clumsy,' 217
15. follows : — White,— Thompson,— Ingles, 200, 213
16. Omit comma. 208
17. air mail : 213
18. Omit comma. 209

**Page 72**

1. C 201
2. that 169
3. movie, a—sort, 204
4. that 173a
5. possible, he conceded, 205
6. Omit comma after *are.* 208
7. meeting, 199
8. Omit comma. 208

*Page 72, Cont'd*
9. that 168
10. Flickering, 201
11. C 173
12. visitors, 203

*Page 72, Cont'd*
13. as though 165
14. 1943 : canned—
    vegetables,
    meat, butter,
    213, 200

*Page 72, Cont'd*
15. Omit last
    comma. 208
16. nor 171
17. unless 166

*Page 72, Cont'd*
18. weapon,—pistol,
    204
19. 'I'll—nine,' 217
20. or 171a

**Page 73\***
1. July.  He 230
2. Spencer, who was—manager, was
   experienced, efficient, and courteous. 232
3. woods, John was halted quickly by
   a signal 234
   (woods, John halted quickly at a
   signal)
4. Unless the parts are painted, they
   should 235
5. drawing, Bill next undertook 234
6. The box, which was—wood, and had
   —lid, was lying 232
   (box lying—table was made—wood
   and had—lid.)
7. steps, Susan saw the 234
8. Jeanne plays the violin well, but 235
   (wants to be a better one.)
9. roof, he found a—hole which—repaired. 234
10. again.  It 230
11. C 234
12. When Jerry had written—supplies,
    he—it, put it into an envelope,
    and mailed it. 232
13. Because Jack was very hungry, the
    —him. 234
14. rings.  It 230
15. hurrying, the workmen installed 234
16. had the tooth pulled. 235

**Page 74**
1. Make the reference clear. 243
   (When—in, I told)
   (I told her to—receipt when)
2. working in photography 235
   (expert at photography)
3. are made by throwing on 241
4. off.  Ray 230
5. Omit *it*. 239
6. cake, sift 234
7. Make meaning clear. 238
   (balance and that the)
   (balance, and the) 229

\*See footnote on page 191.

*Page 74, Cont'd*
8. When the report is typed, send it
   236
9. said beforehand 243
10. While I was standing 236
11. is that in which 241
12. Omit *them*. 239
13. Make the reference clear. 243
    (When she—job, Mr. Smith advised)
    (Mr. Smith—Mary to be punctual
    when)
14. but that they 238
15. shopping, I was tempted by 236
16. It was a large red book with fine—
    margins. 232
17. paint the legs of the chairs 235
18. When it has been painted, allow 236
19. Make the reference clear. 243
    (On—home, Margaret)
    (Margaret—me to buy—bread on)

**Page 75**
1. and advertising copy writer 244
2. you should 247
3. Although the tire was patched—use
   it. 236
4. eggs, and bread, 245
5. slowly.  Nevertheless, he 249
   (slowly, but)
6. or to remain 246
7. soup and vegetables 245
8. finally sanded it. 247
9. and do 244
10. wanted not only 246
11. C 238
12. enough, but I 249
13. and fences, 245
14. nor to practice it. 246
15. Saturday, but instead I 249
16. is to standardize 241
17. that she does. 247

**Page 76**
1. as 165
2. Beautiful, lofty, 201

### Page 76, Cont'd

3. Army. He 230
4. Make meaning clear. 238
   (but that he)
   (left. He) 231
5. Omit comma. 209
6. that 169
7. read and write and 245
8. That 173
9. C 243
10. judgment, he asserted, 205
11. darkness, flares—ship terrified the 234
12. Omit comma. 209
13. While I was at home, 236
14. *Funeral in Eden* 221
15. meet either 246
16. are 247
17. 'I told—so,' 217
18. Omit *them.* 239
19. where to report 244

### Page 77

1. lighted and ventilated, and had 232
2. remark, 203
3. and shouting, 244
4. said, 'The—grinding,' 217
5. typewriter, Ethel wrote a long letter before she 234
6. is a document ordering a person 241
7. Omit comma. 208
8. C 247
9. *The Adventures of Tom Sawyer* 221
10. If you are unable—, a message 236
    (duty, you should send)
11. popcorn, and candy, 245
12. Make reference clear. 243
    (When he came in, the guard)
    (his pass when he)

### Page 77, Cont'd

13. smoke, he believed, 205
14. Omit comma. 209
15. Make meaning clear. 238
    (and that he will)
    (job. He) 231
16. I not only studied the 246
17. old. Nevertheless, I 249
18. highway. We 230
19. allotted, and 199
20. window, one can see clearly 234

### Page 78

1. will 62
2. illustrating 244
3. C
4. he 77b
   mind, 203
5. with 161
6. Omit comma. 209
   that 173a
7. If photographs are 236
8. who 84a
9. C
10. will,—sure, 205
11. will 57
12. Sawyer and Drake's 101a
    Omit comma. 208
13. and the back 125
14, 15. copy, I thought these pages seemed rather crowded. 234, 134
16. who looks 51
17. C
18. clear, 201
19. is 42
    as 165
20. May 31
21. C

### Page 79

1. is 41
2. lend 35
3. took 34
4. was 43
5. are 41a
6. loan 35
7. take 34
8. were 41a
9. take 34
10. has 43
11. is 41

### Page 79, Cont'd

12. does 41
13. lend 35
14. have 43
15. decide 41a
16. was 41
17. bring 34
18. are 43
19. are 41a
20. finds 41
21. lend 35

### Page 80

1. are 44
2. has 47
3. is 46
4. are 52
5. encircle 48
6. was 47
7. is 46
8. was 44
9. is 49
10. were 48

### Page 80, Cont'd

11. includes 47
12. is 52
13. is 49
14. accompanies 44
15. is 46
16. had primed 53
17. do 48
18. had painted 53
19. deals 47
20. are 52

## Page 80, Cont'd
21. is 46
22. had tried 53
23. have 44

## Page 81
1. will 62
2. have been 63
3. will 62a
4. to drop 65
5. should 62c
6. has 66
7. shall 62
8. to meet 65
9. not soaked him 63
10. shall 62a
11. will 62
12. do not have 66
13. would 62c
14. to interpret 65
15. shall 62a
16. was 66
17. would 62c
18. was 66
19. will 62
20. be 65
21. will say 63
22. would 62c
23. will 62a
24. has worked 63

## Page 82
1. seems 49
2. is 52
3. seems 41
4. shall go 63
5. has 46
6. would 62c
7. took 34
8. was 43
9. shall 62
10. are 41a
11. Have you 66
12. were 48
13. was 44
14. shall 62a
15. had damaged 53
16. lend 35
17. is 47
18. read 65
19. should 62c

## Page 83
1. invites 43
2. had drained 53
3. were 66
4. C 41a
5. is 52
6. to say 65
7. was 41
8. is 49
9. should 62c
10. lend 35
11. were 48
12. will do so 63 (driven and will drive carefully)
13. Take 34
14. was 47
15. will 62a
16. is 49
17. C 46
18. to get 65
19. C 44
20. Jones will 62 I shall 62
21. answers 41
22. were 43
23. has 52

## Page 84
1. whoever 84d
2. Whomever 84c
3. them 86
4. whoever 84d
5. him 86
6. whoever 84d
7. Who 85
8. whoever 84d
9. him 86
10. his 88
11. Whom 85
12. whomever 84c
13. whoever 84d
14. him 86
15. whoever 84d
16. Whom 85
17. Whomever 84c
18. his 88
19. whoever 84d
20. her 86
21. whomever 84c
22. him 86

## Page 85
1. his 88
2. his 89
3. its 92
4. him 91
5. his 88
6. her 90
7. its 89
8. his 91
9. his 88
10. its 89
11. his 91
12. his 90
13. he 88
14. they 92
15. his 88
16. its 92
17. his 90
18. its 92
19. its 89
20. their 92
21. his 91
22. its 89
23. his 88

## Page 86
1. you 96a
2. windows of the house 103
3. someone else's 102a
4. This notice says 98
5. he 96a
6. The plates of a storage battery 103
7. The article says 98
8. The—made 99
9. His 104
10. That—told 98
11. them 97
12. I 96a
13. nobody else's 102a
14. your 104
15. them 97
16. he was called 99
17. His 104
18. Anyone else's 102a

## Page 87
1. Who 85
2. whoever 84d
3. her 88
4. it 97
5. Whomever 84c
6. he puts 91
7. she 96a
8. her 86
9. its 92
10. Are there 99
11. The appearance —floor 103
12. This book says 98
13. your 104
14. his 89
15. its 90
16. Someone else's 102a
17. Whomever 84c
18. my 104

## Page 88
1. took 34
2. C 86
3. his 88
4. is 44
5. C 84d
6. is 41
7. shall 62
8. he 91
9. are 43
10. displaces 52
11. their 92
12. Your 104
13. his 89
14. C 103
15. he 96a
16. is 46
17. The paper says 98
18. it 97
19. People traveled 99 (Travelers went)
20. C 85
21. was 41

## Page 89
1. C 85
2. it 97

*Page 89, Cont'd*

3. cover of the book 103
4. C 84c
5. he is 91 (one is)
6. whoever 84d
7. its 89
8. whoever 84d
9. their 92
10. C 86
11. Frank's 104
12. C 88
13. The article said 98
14. his 88
15. whoever 84d
16. I 96a
17. his 88
18. his—he 91 (one's—one)
19. beautiful—is made 99
20. herself 90
21. you 96a
22. Smith's 104

**Page 90**

1. best 119
2. more nearly 122
3. fewer 123
4. any other 120
5. Fewer 123
6. prettier 119
7. more nearly 122
8. any other 120
9. fewer 123
10. unique 122
11. better 119
12. any other 120
13. more nearly square 122
14. Fewer 123
15. shrewder 119
16. more nearly empty 122

**Page 91**

1. and 125a
2. ask bluntly 138
3. very much 137
4. spent nearly 139
5. and 127a

*Page 91, Cont'd*

6. and 125a
7. estimate quickly 138
8. too much 137
9. and 127a
10. and 125a
11. came only 139
12. too greatly 137
13. broke nearly 139
14. read carefully 138
15. endure this only 139
16. and 127a
17. very much 137
18. think first 138
19. and 125a
20. saw almost 139

**Page 92**

1. to be 65
2. any other 120
3. Whomever 84c
4. C 41
5. fewer 123
6. they 92
7. and rambling 127a
8. too sharply 137 (too much)
9. is 52
10. whoever 84d
11. more nearly 122
12. end of the street 103
13. me 86
14. her 88
15. C 41a
16. read almost 139
17. I 96a
18. C 123
19. shall 62a
20. C 119
21. The picture shows 98
22. is 46
23. clean the carburetor thoroughly 138
24. never had gone 63

**Page 93**

1. divided 148
2. in that 151
3. on October 12 149
4. was of 152
5. start 148
6. was of 152
7. in this 151
8. on Easter 149
9. was of 152
10. in that 151
11. on March 12 149
12. expanded 148
13. behind 150
14. in that 151
15. investigating 148
16. behind 150
17. of no use 152
18. near 148

**Page 94**

1. into 154
2. from 157
3. with 159
4. between 153
5. into 154
6. at 159 with 159
7. among 153
8. from 157
9. at 159
10. into 154
11. among 153
12. from 157
13. with 159
14. between 153
15. from 157
16. with 159
17. into 154
18. between 153
19. from 157
20. among 153
21. at 159
22. into 154
23. from 157

**Page 95**

1. runs 41
2. most nearly 122
3. C 85

*Page 95, Cont'd*

4. on 149
5. he 96a
6. best 119
7. were 44
8. and prompt 127a
9. of little 152
10. too badly 137
11. C 88
12. from 157
13. C 152
14. and saucer 125a
15. Omit *up.* 148
16. The speaker's stand is called 99
17. among 153
18. with 159
19. C 53
20. behind 150
21. into 154
22. recognize almost 139
23. fewer 123

**Page 96**

1. whether 174
2. as the old, if not brighter 172
3. so that 175
4. as the cold, if not worse 172
5. whether 174
6. so that 175
7. whether 174
8. as molasses, if not thicker 172
9. so that 175
10. whether 174
11. as it was worth, if not more 172
12. so that 175
13. whether 174
14. as was wise, if not longer 172
15. whether 174
16. so that 175

**Page 97**

1. any other 120

*Page 97, Cont'd*
2. very much 137
3. On Monday 149
4. fewer 123
5. divide 148
6. won nearly 139
7. best 119
8. of no use 152
9. and 127a
10. with 159
11. more nearly 122
12. whether 174
13. behind 150
14. into 154
15. and 125a
16. nail the lid on next 138
17. as the light was good, if not longer 172
18. in that way 151
19. among 153
20. so that 175
21. from 157

Page 98
1. was 88
2. Omit *in.* 148
3. more 119 longer 119
4. was 41
5. as his brother, if not better 172
6. Who 85
7. behind 150
8. whether 174
9. too badly 137
10. has 47
11. as it snowed last winter, if not more 172
12. any other 120
13. Whomever 84c
14. expands 52 freezes 52
15. so that 175
16. between 153
17. C 154

*Page 98, Cont'd*
18. C 44
19. so that 175
20. In this way, 151
21. Llamas are used 99
22. whether 174
23. it seemed that you would never 139

Page 99
1. Omit second *a.* 127a
2. any other 120
3. Omit *up.* 148
4. among 153
5. Behind 150
6. more 119
7. To refuse the request completely 138
8. whether 174

*Page 99, Cont'd*
9. on Saturday 149
10. among 153
11. from 157
12. as strong as the finest—used, if not stronger 172
13. more nearly round 122
14. Omit *in.* 148 Omit *up.* 148
15. into 154
16. C 157
17. very much moved 137
18. in this way 151
19. worked here only 139
20. so that 175
21. with 159
22. Fewer 123
23. of no use 152

Page 100*
1. Omit comma. 226, 202
2. John, who—physics, 226a, 202
3. This model, which—prize, has 233a, 202
4. Mr. Grover, who—collector, you know, permitted me 237 (bookplates, which he collects, you know.)
5. C 226, 202
6. an etching by Bewick, who 237 (for which he was famous)
7. coat,—tailored, 226a, 202
8. records by Bing Crosby 237
9. Omit comma. 226, 202
10. plane, which—faster, rather 233a, 202
11. hair,—curly, 226a, 202
12. C 226a, 202
13. Omit comma. 226, 202
14. enunciation of the announcer 237

Page 101
1. Because of 248
2. and which had 238a
3. cut and the typing is accurate, the copies—satisfactory. 242
4. realized that 240

*Page 101, Cont'd*
5. and when I am busy 238a
6. card, which he asked me to send you. 237 (card belonging to Martin, who)
7. sealed and stamped the envelope, George—check. 242
8. feels that 240
9. and when 238a
10 C 248
11. Omit comma. 226, 202
12. because of 248 (Jerry's rapid advance—was due to)
13. that 240
14. raining and she didn't—umbrella, Sue wore—office. 242
15. calendar,—week, 226a, 202
16. Lowell's recovery—was due to 248

Page 102
1. Take 34
2. his 88
3. on Friday 149
4. as well as a native, if not better 172
5. any other mountain 120
6. I 96a
7. fewer 123

**Page 102, Cont'd**

8. C 226a, 202
9. from 157
10. is 52
11. whether 174
12. Omit *up*. 148
13. who 85
14. and when you expect 238a
15. moved here only 139
16. Mr. Weber, 226a, 202
17. their 43
18. too much amused 137
19. come in and see Albert, don't—surprised. 242
20. Because of 248
21. C 84c
22. childhood home of my aunt, who 237
23. angry at 159

**Page 103**

1. Omit comma. 202, 226
2. After the dinner he 233a

**Page 103, Cont'd**

3. because of 248
4. book,—Wilson, 202, 226a
5. received a note from Glenn, whom 237
6. born and where 238a
7. Because of 248
8. Omit comma. 202, 226
9. found in the contract a clause that 233a
10. thinks that 240
11. Hardy, who 202, 226a
12. C 202, 226a
13. aspirin and lie down, you—headache. 242
14. knew that 240
15. Roberts,—well, 202, 226a
16. hall and waited—Hubbard, Mrs. Archer—in. 242
17. warned us that 240
18. files, which contain 237
    (files, which have)

**Page 104**

1. lain 30
2. C 36
3. well 111
4. its 102
5. beautifully 110
6. have 61
7. C 80
8. Greek 180
9. Ought we not 60
10. me, Grant, 211
11. right; I 229
    (right, since)
    (right. I)
12. admiral 189a
13. loud 117
14. Springfield, Ohio, 206
15. C 100b
16. her 81a
17. Omit quotation marks. 215
18. C 79
19. West 187
20. Make separate sentences. 231
    (blocks, so—store. We—some, but)

**Page 105**

21. mentions 42
22. very 113
    (really)
23. C 81b
24. Omit *of*. 140
25. surely 112
    (certainly)
26. is 40b
27. C 77b
28. and the 125
29. Omit comma. 208
30. have 51
31. Omit second *a*. 128
32. who 84a
33. partners, 203
34. should 56
35. that 173a
36. Omit second *a*. 126
37. Post 101a
38. may 57
39. may 31
40. of 162
41. Shall 62b
42. following: 213
43. election, I—remark, 205

**Page 105, Cont'd**

44. with 161
45. is one in which 241
46. Omit comma. 209

**Page 106**

47. and biographies 245
48. but 164b
49. Make reference clear. 234
    (carefully, we hear)
    (As we listen)
50. as 165
51. Unless the coat is—wear it again. 236
52. us. Her 230
53. 'Excuse me,' 217
54. blueprint reading 244
55. better 119
56. Who 85
57. has 41
58. Omit *up*. 148
59. Whomever 84c

**Page 106, Cont'd**

60. as Joan, if not better 172
61. C 153
62. whoever 84d
63. their 92
64. clerk, who—typist, 202, 226a
65. from—customer a letter which 233a
66. fewer 123
67. into 154
68. is 52
69. Omit commas. 202, 226
70. C 86
71. on 149
72. shall 62a
73. his 88
74. he 96a
75. which was singing in opera 237
    (career of his son, who)

# INDEX

(Unless otherwise indicated, numbers refer to rules in the Reference Section.)

202

# DATE DUE